The Open University

Science: a level 3 course

S339

Understanding the Continents

Block 4

Mountain Building

Prepared for the Course Team
by Nigel Harris and John Whalley

The S339 Course Team

Chair
Nigel Harris

Course Manager
Jessica Bartlett

Other members of the Course Team

Mandy Anton *(Designer)*
Gerry Bearman *(Editor)*
Steve Blake *(Author)*
Steve Drury *(Author)*
Nigel Harris *(Block 4 Chair, Author)*
Martin Kemp *(BBC Producer)*
Dave McGarvie *(Author)*
Jann Matela *(Word Processing)*

Ray Munns *(Cartographer)*
Pam Owen *(Graphic Artist)*
Professor Julian Pearce, University of
    Wales, Cardiff *(Course Assessor)*
Nick Rogers *(Block 2 Chair, Author)*
Hazel Rymer *(Author)*
Val Russell *(original Course Manager)*
John Whalley *(Consultant Author)*

The Course Team gratefully acknowledges the contributions of those who produced the first editions of this Course, from which parts of this Block have been derived. In addition, we would like to thank the students, Associate Lecturers and assessors from other institutions who commented on drafts of this new edition. Other contributors to S339 are acknowledged in specific credits.

The Open University, Walton Hall, Milton Keynes MK7 6AA.

First published 2001.

Edited, designed and typeset by The Open University.

Printed and bound in the United Kingdom by The Bath Press, Glasgow, UK.

ISBN 0 7492 3551 9

This block forms part of an Open University course, S339 *Understanding the Continents*. The complete list of texts which make up this course can be found at the back. Details of this and other Open University courses can be obtained from the Course Reservations and Sales Office, PO Box 724, The Open University, Milton Keynes MK7 6ZS, United Kingdom: tel. (00 44) 1908 653231. For availability of this or other course components, contact Open University Worldwide Ltd, The Berrill Building, Walton Hall, Milton Keynes MK7 6AA, United Kingdom: tel. (00 44) 1908 858585, fax (00 44) 1908 858787, e-mail ouwenq@open.ac.uk

Alternatively, much useful course information can be obtained from the Open University's website, http://www.open.ac.uk

3.1

Contents

1   Introduction

Mountains result from two opposing processes — uplift and erosion. For as long as uplift is faster than erosion, mountains are created and increase in altitude through time. Once uplift slows down, or erosion accelerates, the mountains are whittled away until, eventually, all that is left is their roots. This process is known as **exhumation** and results in deeper levels of the crust being exposed. The roots of ancient mountain ranges are particularly useful for geologists because they provide a window into processes active deep in the crust during mountain building.

The uplift of continental rocks that results in the Earth's great mountain ranges is an isostatic response to crustal thickening. So the question of 'how are mountains made?' can be recast as 'how does the crust thicken?'. The crust can thicken by purely igneous processes, for example by underplating, but more commonly thickening of the crust results from deformation. This means that ancient mountain roots can be recognized by strongly deformed belts of rocks; these are termed **orogenic belts**. Orogenic belts may be young and mountainous like the Alps or Himalaya, or old and relatively flat like the Limpopo Belt in southern Africa or the Highlands of Scotland, but all orogenic belts are largely made up of intensely deformed and metamorphosed rocks.

1.1   Collision zones

The stress fields in the lithosphere that are responsible for major deformation events result from the relative movements of the plates that make up the Earth's surface skin. These stresses are transmitted over long distances through the lithosphere but they are most intense on and around the plate margins.

● What are the three possible relative motion vectors that determine the nature of plate margins?

● Plates can move towards each other, away from each other, or slide past each other, giving rise to destructive, constructive or conservative margins.

Each of these margins show a characteristic assemblage of deformation features. Whilst important deformation events are evident in the rocks formed along both constructive and conservative margins, we concentrate, in this Block, on the features associated with plate convergence because it is here, at the destructive margins, that the classic orogenic belts are formed.

Destructive margins may undergo a long history of oceanic plate subduction, as seen in the present western margin of South America, but ultimately many are terminated by continental collision. For example, the northward subduction of thousands of kilometres of Indian oceanic crust was terminated by the arrival and collision of the Indian sub-continent and formation of the Himalayan orogenic belt. In this Block we will examine zones where the convergence of two or more plates has ultimately brought blocks of continental crust into contact with one another. These are known as **collision zones**.

Figure 1.1 shows a section through an idealized collision zone between two major continents at two stages during its evolution. In the upper diagram, we can identify the major geological components which characterize the situation before collision. Oceanic lithosphere is being subducted beneath the upper

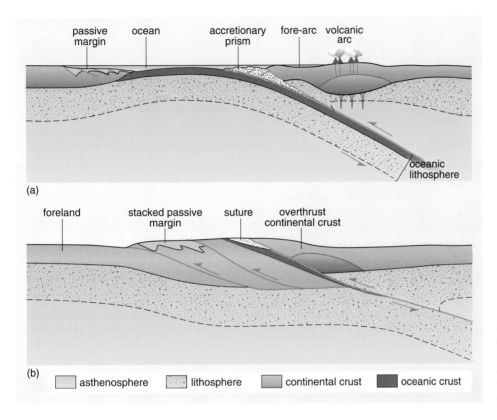

Figure 1.1 Cartoon illustrating continental collision, (a) convergence before collision, narrowing the ocean basin; (b) convergence after collision, thickening the continental crust by thrusting.

plate and a volcanic arc is formed. The active continental margin of this over-riding plate is marked by an accretionary prism composed of slices of oceanic sediments that have escaped subduction. The passive continental margin of the downgoing plate is marked by extensive shelf sediments lying between the ocean and the continental interior.

Eventually (Figure 1.1b), the leading edge of the continent on the downgoing plate enters the subduction zone but the buoyancy of the continental crust prevents subduction from continuing. In order to even partially subduct, material must deform extensively but, once subduction has ceased, the energy of the system has to be dissipated by other processes. The result is further deformation that affects both plates. This deformation initiates along the plane of contact between the two plates but, over time, it migrates out to affect more and more of the lower plate. Crustal shortening is accompanied by significant thickening, and this thickened lithosphere is isostatically unstable, resulting in topographic uplift.

A glance at the *Geological Map of the World* will confirm that the more obvious young mountain belts, such as the Himalaya, the Alps and the Andes, are broadly linear features that are widely scattered on the Earth's surface. But it would be a mistake to conclude that orogenic belts are an unusual feature of continental crust. Older orogenic belts often have more diffuse margins but comprise a significant proportion of the continents. The older the belt, the more likely it is to preserve only fragments of the full picture. However, older belts provide good insight into mid–lower crustal deformation and we are fortunate in Britain in having a classic example of such a belt in the Caledonides. Much of Africa is made up of old orogenic belts, formed during the Pan-African orogeny, enclosing nuclei of Archean cratons. If the Pan-

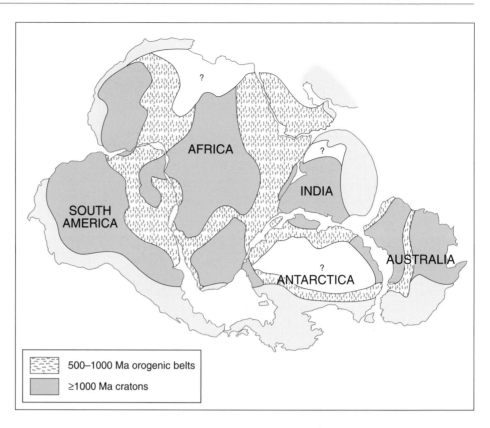

Figure 1.2 The distribution of orogenic belts of Pan-African age (500–1000 Ma) on the reconstructed supercontinent of Gondwana.

African orogenic belts of a reconstructed Gondwana are sketched out (Figure 1.2), they are seen to criss-cross the supercontinent. Each one is characterized by intense deformation and metamorphism.

The Gondwanan orogenic belts represent ancient collision zones which mark the sutures between the smaller plates that eventually made up the supercontinent. Collision tectonics has been one of the most important processes that determine the growth of continents throughout the evolution of the continental lithosphere. The geological information locked up in orogenic belts is essential for understanding the nature of these collisions.

1.2   The Himalayan collision

The most recent example on Earth of a collision between two continents, and the most spectacular example of mountain building, is the Himalaya. The processes that led to this collision and which also formed the present-day paleogeography around the Indian Ocean, can be traced back to the break up of Gondwana over 100 Ma ago.

1.2.1   Break-up of Gondwana

Reconstruction of plate movements since the end of the Jurassic is based partly on paleomagnetic pole positions and partly on the magnetic anomalies in the Indian Ocean. The initial rifting of India (on the same plate as Madagascar at that time) from Africa occurred 130 Ma ago (Figure 1.3). By 120 Ma, India had rifted from Antarctica and began its northwards drift.

Rifting is commonly accompanied by magmatism and, on Figure 1.3, the areas of Early Cretaceous lava are shown to be concentrated around the continental margins of the Gondwanan fragments. All the lavas shown are continental flood basalts which are overwhelmingly olivine tholeiites in composition, similar to the Red Sea magmatism formed after lithospheric thinning had begun. By the Late

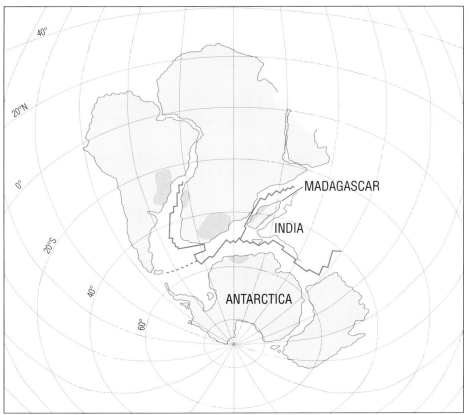

Figure 1.3 Early Cretaceous (~120 Ma) reconstruction of the southern continents. Red lines show constructive margins responsible for the break-up of India from Africa and Madagascar. Purple shaded regions show distribution of Early Cretaceous basaltic magmatism related to rifting in the Southern Hemisphere.

Cretaceous (80 Ma), the Indian Ocean had begun to form following rifting between Madagascar and India (Figure 1.4). The large province of flood basalts in NW India, the Deccan Traps, are Late Cretaceous to Paleogene in age (60–70 Ma) and are probably related to that rifting event. The Deccan Traps are over 2000 m thick in places and are believed to extend for a thousand kilometres from India offshore to the Seychelles Islands to the west.

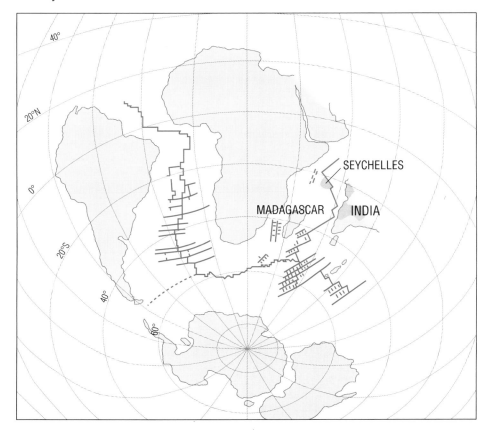

Figure 1.4 Late Cretaceous/ Paleogene (~65 Ma) reconstruction of the southern continents. Red lines show constructive margins responsible for spreading in the South Atlantic and Indian Ocean. Purple shaded regions show distribution of Late Cretaceous basaltic magmatism.

Details of post-Cretaceous plate movements in the Indian Ocean are fairly complex because spreading ridges and triple junctions reorganized themselves to form the three ridge systems now active in the Indian Ocean. You should confirm on the *Geological Map of the World* that these comprise the Carlsberg, South-West Indian and South-East Indian ridges. The triple junction is known as the Rodriguez triple junction.

During the Paleogene (about 50 Ma ago), relative movement between the Australian and Indian Plates ceased, so that today Australia and India are part of the same plate. Since that time, both continents have drifted north together by spreading along the Carlsberg and South-East Indian ridges. It is this northward movement that has resulted in subduction of South-East Asia along the Sunda arc and in collision along the Himalayan orogen.

1.2.2 The northward movement of India

The Tethys Ocean lay between India and Eurasia at the beginning of the Tertiary (Figure 1.5). The convergence of the two continents resulted from ocean-ridge spreading to the south in the infant Indian Ocean and subduction of the Tethyan lithosphere to the north. The positions of India relative to Eurasia have been established in some detail, both from studies of the Indian Ocean magnetic anomalies and paleomagnetic pole positions.

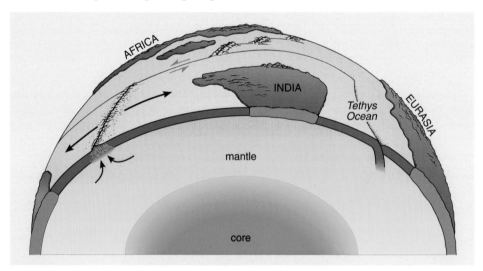

Figure 1.5 Sketch showing the northward movement of India during the Paleogene, causing a shrinking Tethys Ocean to the north.

Figure 1.6 shows the convergence of India on Asia over the past 70 Ma, keeping Asia fixed in its present position. The positions are plotted at irregular time intervals because they are determined from particular magnetic reversals recorded in the Indian Ocean.

● Does Figure 1.6 record a consistent direction of convergence between India and Asia?

● In general, yes, but between 50 and 48 Ma there was a distinct judder of India to the east as can be seen from the paths A′–A or B′–B.

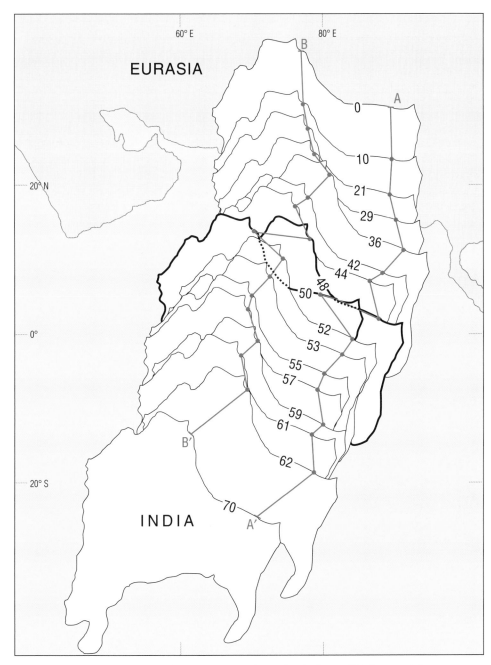

Figure 1.6 Cenozoic northward drift of India from 70 Ma (numbers on northern margin of India indicate time in Ma at that position). Also plotted is the motion of two points (A′ and B′) now located on the Indian continent near the northern margin of India (A and B). The position of Asia is kept arbitrarily fixed in its present position.

So, the relative movement direction was disturbed about 50 Ma ago. The positions shown on Figure 1.6 can be translated into average rates of convergence between India and Asia (Figure 1.7).

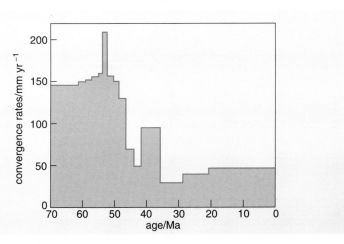

Figure 1.7 Computed rate of convergence between the Indian and Asian Plates over the past 70 Ma.

Question 1.1 Combining the information on both position and speed for the two converging lithospheric fragments, identify (from Figures 1.6 and 1.7) different phases in the drift history of India relative to Asia. From your answer, when do you think collision between India and Asia occurred?

In fact, there is some argument about the precise timing of collision and estimates vary between 60 and 45 Ma. This uncertainty results partly from geologists dating different events from the collision process. It is important to remember that a collision between lithospheric plates is not a single event but a long and complex process. For example, early on, as the intervening ocean basin contracts, deformation of continental margin sediments may precede the obduction of oceanic lithosphere. Much later, crustal thickening resulting from collision will continue for tens of millions of years after the initial impact of the colliding plates.

Question 1.2 What has been the approximate amount of post-collision convergence between stable India (south of the Himalaya) and stable (northern) Asia?

This is an extraordinary result. Remember there was no more oceanic lithosphere between northern India and Asia to be subducted during this period. The shortening resulted largely from the deformation of continental lithosphere.

1.3   Unravelling an orogenic belt

Plate tectonics provides the broad framework within which orogenic events can be described but if we are to understand collision tectonics in any greater detail we have to be able to interpret the processes by which the rocks that make up the mountain belt can change shape. In this Block, we make use of geological evidence taken from several different orogenic belts. This is because no one belt provides evidence of the full range of processes that operate from shallow crustal levels to the lowermost crust.

- Variations in temperature and pressure will result in different deformation mechanisms being dominant at different crustal levels. What are the two broad groupings of deformation mechanisms?

- At high crustal levels, deformation will be dominated by processes of fracture and frictional sliding along the fracture planes, *brittle deformation*. The higher temperatures and pressures at deeper crustal levels favour structures such as folds and shear zones which are examples of *ductile deformation*.

The Alpine belt of southern Europe provides wonderful examples of strongly deformed but largely non-metamorphic sedimentary sequences. We will use the Sub-Alpine Chains of Southern France for most of our examples of high crustal level structures. In contrast, the Caledonides of Northern Britain will be our type locality for lower crustal level structures, but we are fortunate in that a small portion of the high crustal level material is also preserved in the Moine Thrust Belt.

Rocks outcropping within orogenic zones are often complex, but usually provide two main strands of evidence for the geologist to interpret. First, they are deformed. In Sections 2 to 5, we are concerned with deformational processes on a wide range of scales from thin sections to the dimensions of whole mountains. Secondly, many rocks from orogenic belts have been heated during burial and deformation. The study of metamorphic rocks (Section 6) leads to a better understanding of the thermal structure of the lithosphere beneath mountains. This in turn helps the geologist understand the mechanism responsible for crustal thickening and mountain building. In the final Section, we return to the Himalayan orogeny to bring together geophysical, geochemical, structural and metamorphic evidence for interpreting the evolution of a young orogenic belt.

2 Structures produced at high crustal level

It is sensible to start our task of unravelling an orogenic belt by looking at the geometrically simplest structures. Rocks deformed for a shorter period of time will generally suffer less intense deformation and could be expected to carry some of the simplest structures.

⬤ Where should you look for such structures?

⬤ The parts of the orogenic belt where deformation occurred towards the end of the sequence of collision-related events.

Following collision, deformation in the lower plate migrates out from the line of contact, the suture, between the two plates (Figure 1.1). Rocks deformed for the shortest period of time in an orogenic belt are likely to be found in the lower plate at some distance from the suture. This region, which we will term the **Outer Zone**, corresponds to the left-hand side of Figure 1.1b.

Because the first rocks to be deformed are those close to the suture, it is here that the crust initially thickens and is then uplifted by isostasy. This is illustrated in Figure 1.1b where the thrust slice immediately below the suture is being exhumed along the suture which has become a normal fault. At any point in the evolution of the orogen, rocks that lie in the **Inner Zone** close to the suture have been exhumed from deeper crustal levels. In contrast, structures from the Outer Zone are generated at the highest crustal levels. In this Section, we will use examples from the Outer Zone of the Western Alps to illustrate the geometries of high crustal level structures. In order to appreciate the pattern of these structures, we first need to establish the larger-scale features of this part of the Alpine orogenic belt and the stratigraphy of the rock units involved before looking in detail at the structures themselves.

Figure 2.1 A reconstruction of the western end of the Tethys Ocean in Cretaceous times (*c.* 80 Ma). Major plate boundaries (subduction zones, oceanic ridges and transform faults) are shown in red. Coastal outlines are uncertain since they have been greatly modified by the Alpine orogeny.

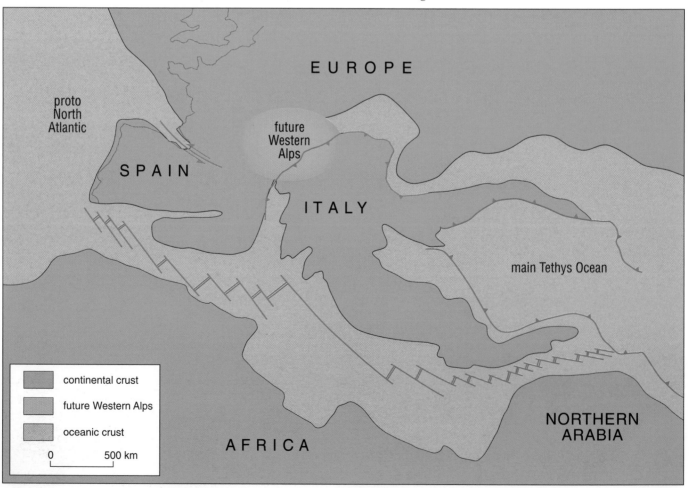

EUROPE

proto North Atlantic

future Western Alps

SPAIN

ITALY

main Tethys Ocean

- continental crust
- future Western Alps
- oceanic crust

0   500 km

AFRICA

NORTHERN ARABIA

The Western Alps are the result of a collision between a continental fragment, which now forms much of modern Italy, and the main continental mass of Europe (Figure 2.1). It is tempting to think of collision zones as being the product of just two major blocks of continental crust coming into contact; in the case of the Alps, these would be Europe and Africa. In reality, though, when a large ocean is subducted there is much material that is relatively buoyant and resists being subducted. These fragments, termed microplates, become trapped between the converging major continental masses and a number of them lay between the continental blocks of Europe and Africa throughout much of the Mesozoic (Figure 2.1).

Figure 2.1 shows that as early as 80 Ma ago, Italy had collided with the southern margin of Europe initiating deformation. The main collision was completed by around 40 Ma but this was by no means the end of tectonic activity, which continued until late Neogene times, around 6 Ma ago. Indeed some minor activity, in the form of earthquakes, continues to the present day.

The resulting anatomy of the Alpine collision zone is shown as a cross-section in Figure 2.2. Immediately to the north-west of the suture, the Inner Zone is comprised of deformed rocks that have been brought up from deep crustal levels. Further away from the suture, the Outer Zone is characterized by deformation of rocks at high crustal levels. The Outer Zone is bounded by the **foreland**, representing the undisturbed part of the European Plate. Uplift and erosion of the orogen have resulted in the deposition of thick post-Alpine sediments, called **molasse**, onto the foreland.

Figure 2.2 Simplified present day cross-section through the Western Alps. Section line is shown on Figure 2.4.

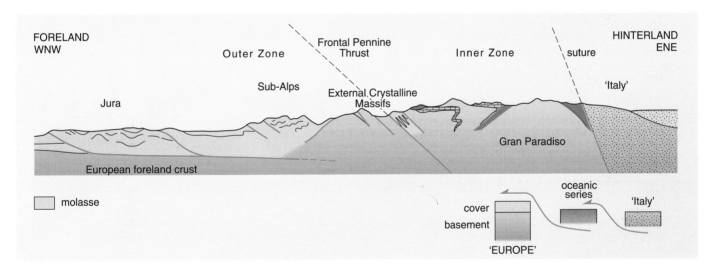

2.1 Tectonic units of the Outer Zone

At the time that the Tethys Ocean began to open, the southern margin of the European plate was composed largely of meta-sedimentary and meta-igneous rocks that had already been involved in a Late Paleozoic orogeny, known as the Variscan orogeny. Throughout the Mesozoic, from the Triassic to the start of the Cretaceous, thick sequences of carbonate sediments were deposited as a **cover** sequence on top of this **basement**. The earliest units to be deposited were

Figure 2.3 A reconstruction of the Alps in cross-section prior to closure of the Tethys Ocean and the collision between Italy and Europe. The scale is approximate because the width of the Inner Zone before collision depends on the model used for the reconstruction.

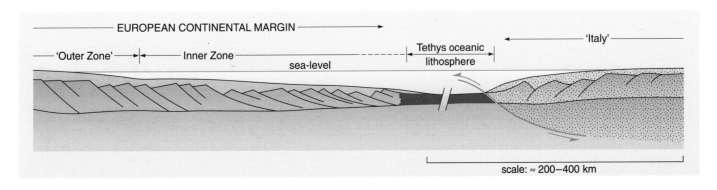

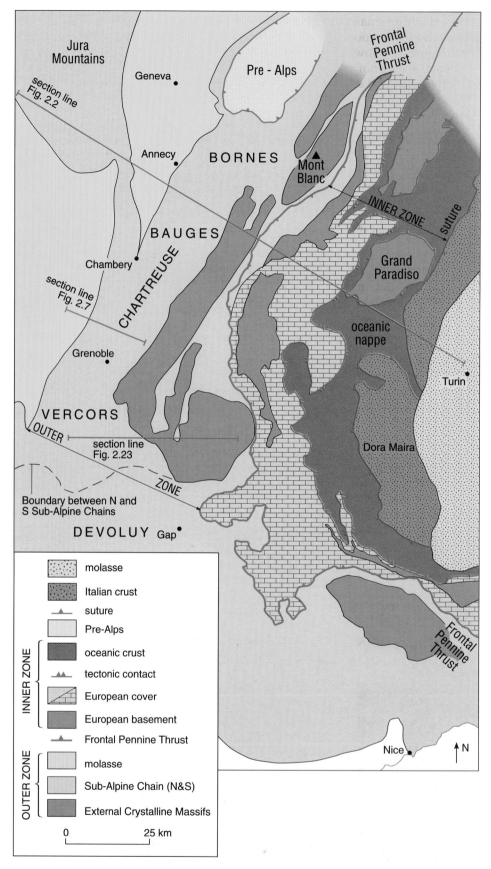

Figure 2.4 Geotectonic sketch map of the Western Alps. The rock units to the south-east of the suture are those of the Italian microplate. The oceanic nappe contains basalts and sediments from the destroyed Tethys Ocean. All the remaining rock units were part of the European Plate before collision.

contained within small fault-bounded basins, but throughout much of the Jurassic and Cretaceous, laterally extensive 'layer-cake' sequences were laid down. Figure 2.3 shows a schematic cross-section through the European continental shelf prior to the collision, when the shelf was several hundred kilometres wide and composed of rocks that, at the present day, are found in both the Outer and Inner Zones of the Alpine belt.

Today, the sedimentary rocks of the Outer Zone form the **Sub-Alpine Chains** (Figure 2.4), typified by high plateaux such as the Chartreuse and Vercors Massifs (Figure 2.5). The metamorphic grade of these rocks is very low. The clay minerals have begun to react to form micas but their grain sizes are small, showing that the reactions have not progressed very far. The Sub-Alpine Chains were formed from a sedimentary succession that was between 4 and 5 km thick and this metamorphic evidence demonstrates that they cannot have been buried significantly deeper than this during their subsequent tectonic evolution.

However, the Outer Zone is not composed solely of uplifted sedimentary rocks. Between the Sub-Alpine Chains and the Inner Zone lie ranges of much higher mountains, the **External Crystalline Massifs**. These are composed of meta-sedimentary and meta-igneous rocks, the composition and ages of which correlate with the pre-Triassic rocks of the foreland. These massifs, then, are part of the European Plate basement.

- Mont Blanc, at 4807 m (Figure 2.6) the highest peak in the Alps, is part of one of these crystalline massifs (Figure 2.4). Assuming that the Triassic to Cretaceous sedimentary succession of the Outer Zone is 4 km thick, what is the amount of uplift that has occurred since the Cretaceous sediments were deposited?

- 4807 m + 4000 m = 8807 m, roughly 8.8 km. This simple calculation could be an overestimate as it assumes that the full cover sequence was originally present on top of the Mont Blanc basement rocks. On the other hand though, it takes no account of how much basement material has already been eroded.

Now that we have identified the pieces of the first part of the Alpine orogenic jigsaw puzzle we can go on to examine some important questions. What is the relationship between the basement rocks of the External Crystalline Massifs and the cover rocks of the Sub-Alpine Chains? How did the Sub-Alpine Chain rocks react to the uplift of the basement massifs?

Figure 2.5 Folded Cretaceous limestones from the eastern Chartreuse Massif, part of the Sub-Alpine Chains of the Western Alps.

Figure 2.6 The Mont Blanc External Crystalline Massif, seen from the west (Savoie, France).

2.2 Thrust zones

The Chartreuse Massif (Figures 2.4 and 2.5) is an excellent example of the style of deformation seen in the Sub-Alpine Chains. A cross-section through the Chartreuse Massif shows a picture that is dominated by faulting (Figure 2.7).

Question 2.1 What type of faults are shown in Figure 2.7?

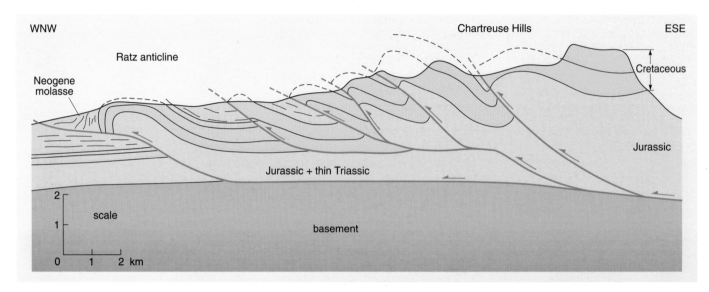

Figure 2.7 Geological cross-section through part of the Chartreuse Massif (Sub-Alpine Chains) illustrating major structures. Section line is shown on Figure 2.4. The Neogene molasse consists of conglomeratic sediments derived by erosion of early Alpine thrust sheets but which are themselves involved in later stages of the thrusting.

There are several other features shown on the cross-section that are characteristic of thrust faults. For example, the fault trajectories when seen in cross-section show a ramp and flat geometry.

⬤ What determines the location of the ramp and flat sections of a thrust fault trajectory?

⬤ These are determined by the relative competences of the rock units. Ramps, the portions of the trajectory that cut across the stratigraphy, occur in the more competent units whilst flats, the portions sub-parallel to stratigraphy, are found in the least competent horizons.

In an Alpine context, the competent units are the stronger, more massive, limestones and the incompetent units are weaker mudrocks, thinly bedded limestones or evaporites.

There are also a number of folds in the cross-section. These commonly occur in the hanging-walls above the thrust ramps, suggesting a close relationship. Such folds are thrust ramp anticlines, typified by the Ratz anticline. They are present solely because when the hanging-wall moves up and over a ramp, the beds must fold in order to maintain contact with the fault plane. For this reason, they are also termed **fault-bend folds**. All the faults shown on the section can be traced eastwards and are seen to join with faults lower in the section. These faults also change stratigraphic level and ultimately become flats running along a particular stratigraphic horizon within rocks of Triassic age.

Evaporite minerals, principally anhydrite and gypsum in the Western Alps, are notably weak and thus easily deformed. They provide an horizon of easy slip for thrust faults and that role is enhanced throughout the Western Alps because of their position at the base of the cover sequence.

Question 2.2 Figure 2.8 is a stratigraphic column for the area covered by Figure 2.7. Identify the stratigraphic horizons that would be most likely to host thrust flats.

The major mechanical discontinuity between the weak evaporitic rocks and the crystalline basement has allowed the entire stratigraphic section of Triassic and younger rocks to detach from the underlying basement and move as a series of thrust sheets towards the west; this is away from the main collision zone and towards the foreland. Thrust zones such as this are typical of the outer zones of orogenic belts and are known as **foreland thrust belts**. The main stratigraphic unit along which they move is referred to as the **detachment horizon**.

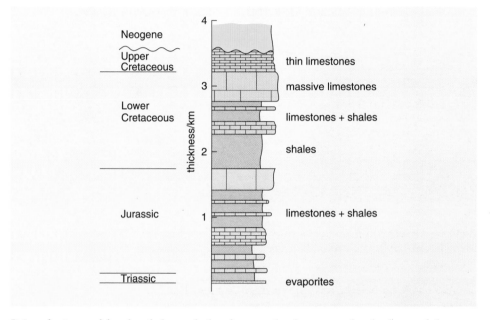

Figure 2.8 Simplified stratigraphic column for the Sub-Alpine Chains.

It is a feature of foreland thrust belts that a **sole thrust** marks the base of the laterally displaced sequence. The thrust sheets above this detachment may have travelled several tens of kilometres towards and over the foreland. Consequently, in their present position they overlie units that did not experience the same stresses and so do not carry the same structural imprint. The term **thin-skinned tectonics** is used to highlight this marked difference in deformation states between the displaced cover and the underlying basement.

The displacement on individual thrusts in Figure 2.7 is at least 2 km and collectively they represent a displacement westwards of the cover sequence of at least 15 km. This represents a small portion of the displacement across the entire Sub-Alpine Chains thrust belt. The cover rocks must originally have rested on top of basement that lay tens of kilometres to the east. So we have answered the first of the questions posed at the end of Section 2.1. The Sub-Alpine Chains are, in part, the detached cover sequence of the External Crystalline Massifs. We also have a preliminary answer to the second question. The Sub-Alpine Chain rocks reacted to the uplift of the basement by detaching and sliding westwards. However, if we look in more detail at the structures present in the Sub-Alpine Chains we will be able to provide a rather fuller answer.

2.2.1 Thrust imbrication

We have already noted the extent to which the thrust faults in Figure 2.7 branch when they are traced from east to west across the section, that is in the direction in which they transport their hanging-walls. This is a feature of all thrust systems and occurs on all scales. It is referred to as thrust imbrication and the smaller thrusts, which branch off, are often referred to as branch lines or splays.

One possible geometry for a group of splay faults is a **duplex**. In this special case, all the splay faults join both above, on the roof fault, and below on the floor fault. The duplex is bounded by these two thrust faults (Figure 2.9).

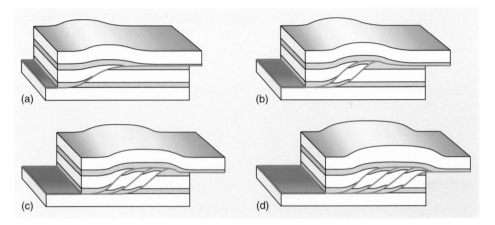

Figure 2.9 The geometry of a duplex. The movement direction is from left to right. For simplicity, no variations in geometry perpendicular to the movement direction have been shown.

Question 2.3 From the photograph in Figure 2.10, identify the roof and the floor thrusts.

Figure 2.10 A duplex within quartzite from the Moine Thrust Belt. The movement direction is parallel to the plane of the photograph.

Clearly, for a duplex to be recognized the splays must join a more major thrust at a higher stratigraphic level. We can see that on Figure 2.7 there is no evidence of this happening.

⬤ Suggest two possible reasons why this is so.

● One possibility is that originally all the smaller thrusts did rejoin to form a duplex but that erosion to the present-day level has removed the evidence. The second possibility is that each splay did not propagate far enough to reach the point where it could rejoin into a more major thrust and so a true duplex never did exist in the area.

When this second possibility occurs, the term **imbricate fan** is used. Figure 2.11 shows typical configurations for both imbricate fans and duplexes.

2.2.2 Lateral variations in thrust geometry

Cross-sections through thrust systems such as Figure 2.7 are usually drawn so that the inferred movement direction of the hanging-wall is parallel to the plane of the section. However, thrust systems, as with all structures, exist in three dimensions. Any fault that is depicted as a line on a cross-section is, in reality, a surface oriented at some angle to the plane of that section.

If we look at a typical thrust system in plan view (Figure 2.12a), the traces of the thrusts are not uniformly parallel. In this view, as in a cross-section, thrusts, in some places, trend parallel to the trace of the bedding and then, in other places, cut across bedding. They also branch and rejoin. Clearly, both the ramp and flat concept and that of imbrication apply in three dimensions. The corresponding cross-section (Figure 2.12b) verifies that the blocks of rock are indeed bounded by faults on all sides.

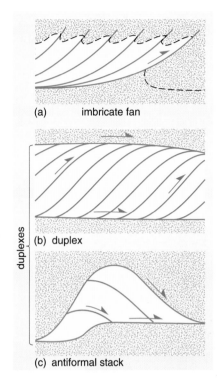

Figure 2.11 Three examples of imbricate thrust systems. An antiformal stack forms when a duplex is deformed during its transport over a ramp in its floor thrust.

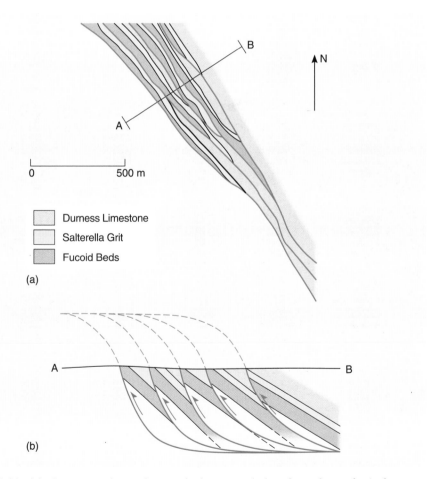

Figure 2.12 (a) Plan view of an imbricate fault system (taken from the geological map of the Moine Thrust Belt, Assynt, NW Scotland). (b) Cross-section along the line A–B. Information from along strike of the faults has been used to reconstruct the eroded top of the duplex.

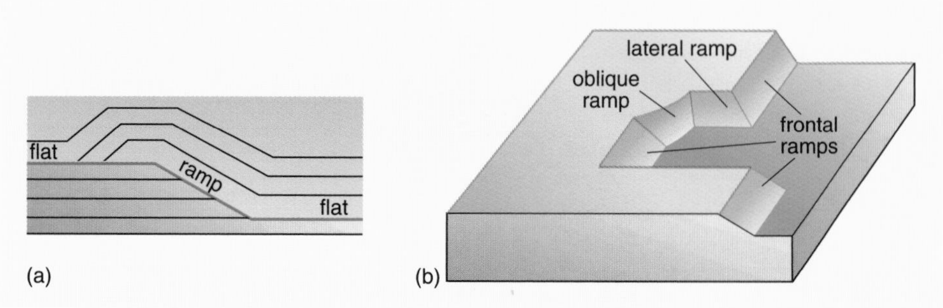

Figure 2.13 (a) Cross-section and (b) block diagram of frontal ramp, lateral ramp and oblique ramp.

The three-dimensional ramp and flat geometry can best be pictured by removing the hanging-wall block from above a ramp (Figure 2.13). The thrust plane cuts across bedding both in a direction normal to the movement direction, where it is termed a frontal ramp, and also in a direction parallel to the movement direction, a lateral ramp. The curving surface between these two extreme orientations forms what is termed an oblique ramp.

Having established the three-dimensional nature of thrust surfaces, it is instructive to look at their appearance in a section taken normal to the movement direction. Figure 2.14 shows how thrust-bounded blocks are stacked one on top of the next in an apparently chaotic pattern. The faults branch extensively but not in the systematic way seen in sections parallel to the movement direction. An interpretation based on sub-areas of Figure 2.14 could lead to any number of erroneous conclusions regarding the movement direction. A comparison of Figures 2.12 and 2.14 illustrates the importance of building up the three-dimensional picture of structures before drawing conclusions.

Figure 2.14 View of imbricate fault system with the movement direction perpendicular to the plane of the photograph (Bude Formation, North Cornwall).

Question 2.4 Figure 2.15 is a map of an imbricate zone. Add labels to the diagram to show the location of a frontal ramp, a lateral ramp and a flat.

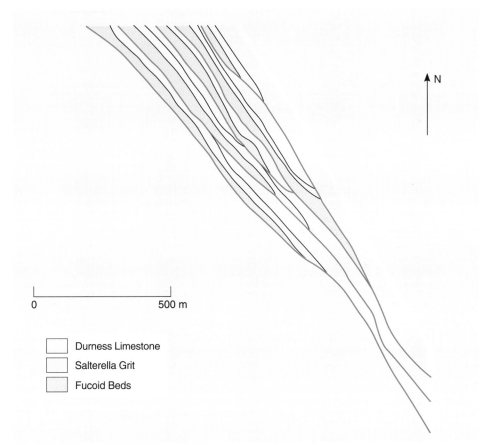

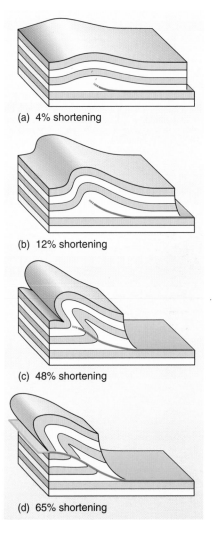

Figure 2.15 Map of imbricate zone (Moine Thrust Belt, NW Scotland).

2.2.3 The association of folding and thrusting

We have already pointed out the Ratz anticline (Figure 2.7) as an example of a fold that is intimately associated with a thrust ramp. It only exists because when the beds are displaced over a non-planar surface they must deform (fold) in order to stay in contact with the fault plane.

⬤ A ramp anticline is an example of a fault-bend fold and as such is a direct consequence of the fault displacement. What is the second type of fold that is associated directly with displacement on faults?

⬤ A tip-related fold (also known as a **fault-tip fold**) takes up the fault's displacement in the volume of rock ahead of its propagating tip (Figure 2.16).

Once the final stage in the development of a fault-tip fold has been reached (Figure 2.16d), the fold continues to evolve as a fault-bend fold as the thrust tip has now propagated beyond the fold.

Figure 2.16 Cartoons showing stages in the development of a fold pair related to a thrust tip. (a) Initially, as the thrust begins to propagate as a ramp, ductile deformation ahead of the thrust tip causes folds to form in the hanging-wall. (b) As the folds grow, they become increasingly asymmetric with a sense of overturning consistent with the direction of the hanging-wall movement. (c) The thrust propagates through the overturned limb of the fold pair. (d) Finally, the anticline in the hanging-wall is carried forward as the thrust tip advances beyond the fold.

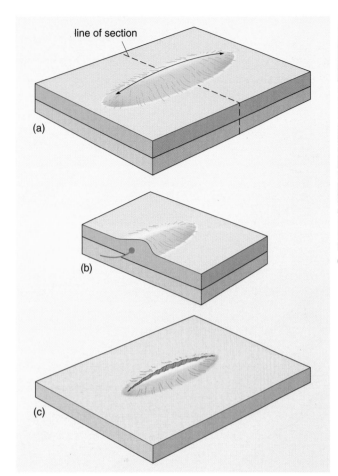

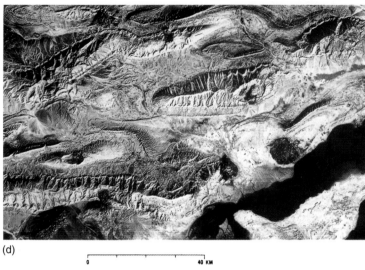

Figure 2.17   (a) A typical pericline showing variations in plunge of axis and amplitude. (b) Cross-section through pericline at position of maximum amplitude. Underlying thrust has its maximum displacement at this point. (c) Variation in displacement along the length of the thrust fault. The displacement decays to zero at the lateral tips. (d) Satellite image of anticlinal periclines, Zagros Mountains, Iran.

As with the other features of thrust faults that we have examined, it is useful to look at the three-dimensional nature of thrust-related folds. Figure 2.17d shows a plan view of thrust tip anticlines. The folds show variable amplitude, the maximum amplitude occurring where the associated thrust carries the largest displacement. When the fold is traced laterally, the amplitude decreases corresponding to a decrease in the displacement carried by the thrust (Figure 2.17a–c). This gives the fold a characteristically periclinal shape, that is one where the fold axes plunge in opposite directions at each end of the axial trace.

Question 2.5   Figure 2.18 is a cross-section through part of the Outer Zone of an orogenic belt upon which are marked a number of structures (a–f). Identify these various structures.

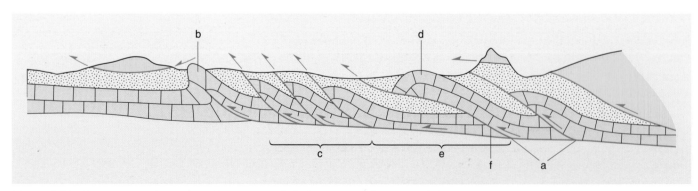

Figure 2.18   Cross-section from part of an orogenic belt Outer Zone, for use with Question 2.5.

2.2.4 Transfer zones

The folds shown in Figure 2.17d each relate to an underlying thrust tip. An individual thrust/fold combination can only affect a finite volume of the rock, but the effect of all of them working together is to maintain the deformation across a much larger volume.

Question 2.6 Figure 2.19 shows the outcrop trace of two neighbouring faults with the displacement shown at points along each fault. Project each displacement measurement on to the reference line by drawing the perpendicular and measure the distance (x) along the reference line that corresponds to each point. Plot the displacements on the graph to show how they vary with distance along the fault trace.

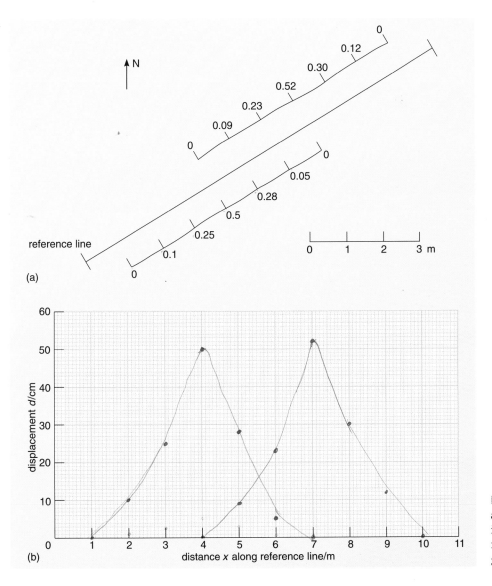

(a)

(b)

Figure 2.19 (a) Plan of fault traces on a bedding plane with displacements (d in metres) recorded at distances (x in metres) along the trace. (b) Blank d/x graph for plotting of data.

Figure 2.17c shows the variation in displacement of an individual thrust but the completed graph in Figure 2.19 shows that as displacement dies away on one fault it is taken up on a neighbouring structure. The volume of rock over which this transfer of displacement takes place is known as a **transfer zone** and these are

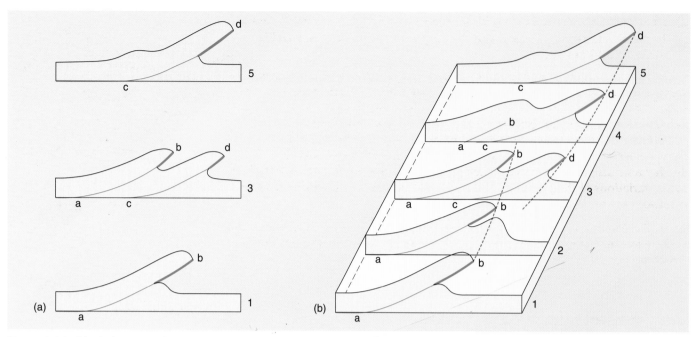

Figure 2.20 Block diagram of a transfer zone between two thrusts (a–b and c–d). Cross-sections 1–5 show the varying proportions to folding and displacement on the two thrusts that bring about the transfer. The total displacement across all the structures must remain constant as the sides of the block are parallel.

often some of the most complexly deformed volumes of rock. Figure 2.20 illustrates the variety of structures that can be found in such zones. It turns out that nearly all structures make use of transfer zones in this way. They are not only characteristic of thrust zones but are also found linking faults and folds in extensional and strike–slip deformation zones.

2.3 Strike–slip zones and linked fault systems

Strike–slip movements dominate the tectonics of many magmatic arcs. However, strike–slip movements also have an important role to play in association with thrust tectonics.

● Look carefully at Figure 2.13, in particular at the area of the fault labelled 'lateral ramp'. Imagine looking vertically down on this fault and draw on the arrows that show the relative movement direction. What type of fault is this?

● The movement on this fault is parallel to the strike of the fault plane. By definition, therefore, it is a strike–slip fault. The sense of relative movement dictates that it is a dextral strike–slip fault.

In other examples, strike–slip faults are seen consistently to displace thrusts (Figure 2.21), and so cannot be interpreted as lateral ramps. It could be argued that the strike–slip faults developed later than the thrusts and thus have no connection with them. However, imagine the situation where an extensive thrust sheet is moving forward over its footwall. There is no requirement for its velocity of movement to be the same at all points along the strike of the fault. Some parts of the thrust sheet may have their movement impeded, perhaps because of along-strike variations in the stratigraphic succession. If this happens, as the movement progresses, some parts of the sheet will move further forward than others.

● How can such variations in the movement pattern be accommodated?

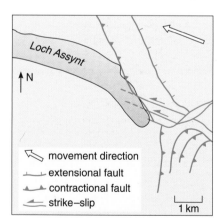

Figure 2.21 Plan view of a thrust belt with associated strike–slip faults. Map of part of the Moine Thrust Belt. Strike–slip faults displace the thrust fault that runs along the shore of Loch Assynt.

In an environment dominated by faulting, the differences are likely to lead to the development of a fault and the displacement on that fault will be strike–slip (Figure 2.22).

Such faults are said to **partition** the deformation, the amount of deformation being different in the blocks on either side of such a fault. Both in this case and in that of the lateral ramp, the thrust faults and strike–slip faults cannot exist independently of each other; they form part of a linked system of faults and displacement on one structure can only be accommodated by matching displacement on the other. Here we have a situation where two sets of faults display a similar linkage to that which we saw between faults and folds. In both cases, variations in the geometry of one set of structures have to be matched by variations in the geometry of the other set.

An understanding of the ways in which structures vary in three dimensions and of the ways in which structures must link together is the key to interpreting structural geometries at all scales from outcrop to orogenic belt.

2.4 Basement reactivation

The picture that we have now built up has concentrated on the response of the sedimentary cover sequence to orogeny. This response is strongly controlled by the stratigraphy in that the weaker horizons determine the location of the major thrusts and the strongest units, thickly-bedded limestones in the case of the Alps, form the mountain ridges and summits.

However, the highest Alpine peaks (Figure 2.6) are composed not of this cover sequence but of the basement massifs. These are metamorphic and igneous

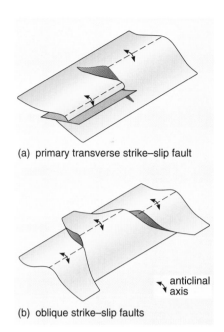

(a) primary transverse strike–slip fault

anticlinal axis

(b) oblique strike–slip faults

Figure 2.22 Strike–slip faults associated with thrusts. The strike–slip faults allow parts of the thrust sheet to be displaced by differing amounts, thus partitioning the deformation. (a) Strike–slip fault perpendicular to the thrust fault. (b) Strike–slip faults oblique to the thrust fault.

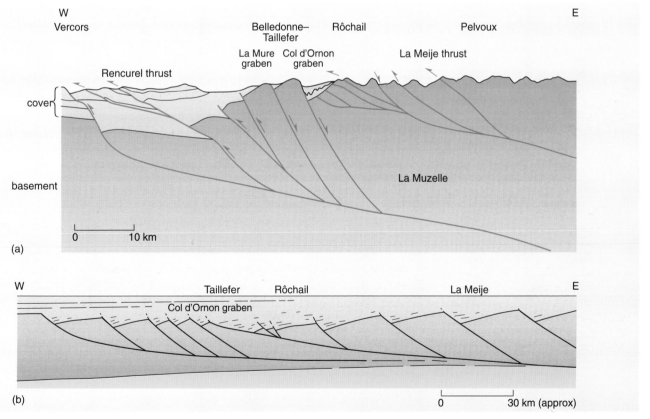

Figure 2.23 (a) Present-day W–E cross-section of area south of Grenoble. Section line is shown on Figure 2.4. (b) W–E cross-section of area south of Grenoble in Late Cretaceous times showing the suggested form of the half-grabens.

rocks, with a highly variable local stratigraphy that cannot exert the same control over the location and style of deformation as the layer-cake stratigraphy of the Sub-Alpine Chains.

The cross-section in Figure 2.23a covers the area from the Vercors Sub-Alpine Chain eastwards across the Belledonne–Taillefer basement massif. The mountains of this basement massif are composed of thrust sheets. In the absence of a layer-cake stratigraphy, what has controlled the positioning of these thrusts?

The answer is shown in Figure 2.23b. Detailed mapping and analysis of the structures has allowed the pre-thrusting configuration of the section to be reconstructed. The subsidence that allowed the accumulation of Triassic and Lower Jurassic sediments had been brought about by the development of fault-bounded, half-graben, basins. We use the term half-graben as the sedimentation is controlled by a fault on only one side. The normal faults in these half-graben developed when the European continental shelf was being stretched as a consequence of the opening up of the Tethys Ocean.

Several of the normal faults in the reconstruction (Figure 2.23b) correspond to present-day thrust faults, most obviously the westernmost fault of the Belledone–Taillefer complex which has given rise to the Rencurel thrust, and the basement thrust slices at La Mure and Col d'Ornon. The reason for this is not difficult to envisage as a pre-existing fracture represents a significant weakness in a body of rock. Subsequent deformation will, wherever possible, make use of the most energy-efficient method available to bring about the necessary shape changes to the rock, and re-using a previous fault satisfies this condition. This process is termed **reactivation**.

Reverse-sense reactivation of normal faults leading to the partial uplift of the basin fill is a common event in the evolution of many sedimentary basins, even though they may be thousands of kilometres away from a collision zone. It is usually referred to as inversion, or more properly as **basin inversion**. The use of the word 'inversion' does not imply that the rocks have been overturned, but rather that the sense of movement has changed from normal (extension) to reverse (compression).

Any previous structure could be reactivated during major tectonic events including those which exist in the basement but which did not originally affect the cover sediments. Further consideration of those effects needs to wait until we have looked at deeper-seated structures.

2.5 Propagate or slip — the fault's dilemma

The above discussion has alerted us to the notion that a fault may have played different roles at different times in its history. Its displacement pattern may be the result of a number of different increments of movement. We will look now at the behaviour of a fault during any one period of its activity.

We can begin with an analogy. Think about moving a piece of heavy furniture that is too heavy to lift and which has to be slid over the floor. If the floor is carpeted, the resistance to movement is normally so high that when you push you usually manage just a short movement before the furniture stops sliding and you must build up your push again. This is exactly how faults move in many circumstances and Figure 2.24 shows how the shear stresses on the fault plane vary as this process continues. The saw-tooth stress curve typifies this style of fault behaviour, usually referred to as **stick–slip** movement. It is the energy release corresponding to each stress drop that generates an earthquake.

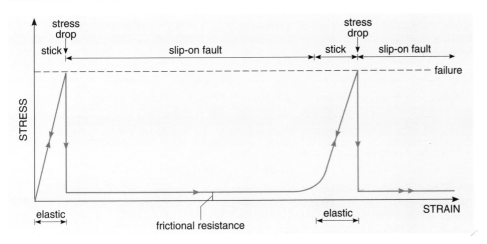

Figure 2.24 The relationship between stress and strain during stick–slip fault movement. Strain here includes fault slip. During the periods of elastic deformation, when no slip takes place, both stress and strain can oscillate in magnitude.

Each stress drop corresponds to an increment of movement on the fault plane but this is not necessarily the only thing that can happen. Many of the structures that we have already described, tip-related folds for example, are associated with the propagation, or growth in physical dimensions, of the fault plane. Figure 2.25a is a cross-section through a fault plane showing the distribution of displacements. This example is a normal fault but the principle is the same for faults with any sense of movement. The displacement is at a maximum in the centre and decays to zero in all directions. This pattern is also seen when looking down onto the fault plane (Figure 2.25b) and so there is a three-dimensional volume of rock that is affected by the displacement.

How does this pattern relate to fault propagation? The fault nucleated at the point that now has the maximum displacement and so this portion of the fault plane has accumulated all subsequent increments of displacement. The fault then propagated away from this nucleation point and so any other point has only accumulated the number of displacement increments that occurred since the fault propagated through that position. Hence, they have smaller displacements because they have suffered fewer increments: in effect, they are a younger portion of the fault plane.

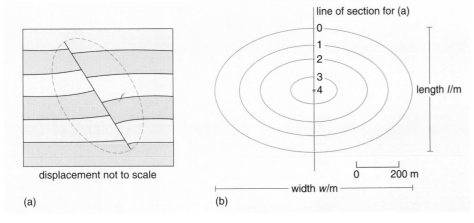

Figure 2.25 (a) Cross-section of a normal fault. Displacement is at a maximum at the centre of the fault trace and dies away to zero at each end. Ductile deformation within the area defined by the ellipse accommodates these variations in displacement. (b) View looking down onto the fault plane with contours showing the variations in displacement within the area affected by ductile deformation.

Each time there is an earthquake on a fault, its energy can be used for some combination of three things: slip on an existing fault plane, propagation of that fault plane or the initiation of a new fault. The typical fault zone with its network of branching shear surfaces is the result of the interplay between these possibilities. However, not all faults exhibit this stick-slip behaviour. Some large faults, the San Andreas Fault being a good example, have some segments that move by stick-slip whilst other parts continually accumulate slip without showing any signs of the discrete energy release associated with earthquakes.

2.6   Rock fabrics associated with upper crustal deformation

So far, we have looked at the deformation that builds mountains in terms of discrete, moderate- to large-sized structures such as folds and faults. The picture that has emerged is one of a network of geometrically linked structures that collectively bring about the deformation of the enormous volumes of rock involved. Furthermore, we have developed the idea that these structures must grow over a period of time, gradually affecting more and more rock. However, all of this large-scale deformation can only develop because mechanisms exist that allow individual grains within the affected rocks to change their shape and size.

2.6.1   Cataclasis

At high crustal levels, temperatures are usually too low to produce significant recrystallization of mineral grains but in the vicinity of faults individual grains will be affected by the fracturing processes which lead to the development of the fault.

- What name is given to the process by which grains are mechanically broken down during faulting?

- This is cataclasis. It consists of the combination of brittle fracturing of grains and the subsequent sliding along fracture surfaces and grain boundaries that occurs when shear stresses are high enough to overcome the frictional resistance.

Fault breccias are one product of cataclasis. In fault breccias, the fragments of the original rock which remain are sufficiently large to be readily visible and a fault breccia is defined as having >50% visible fragments in hand specimen. Breccias, though, are part of a wide range of cataclastic fault rocks that range from coarse breccias down to finely milled rock flours referred to as gouges. The general term **cataclasite** can be used to refer to all fault rocks produced by these fracture-dominated processes.

Figure 2.26 Fault breccia derived from Cretaceous limestone along a thrust in the Chartreuse Massif, French Alps.

Figure 2.26 shows a typical fault breccia from the Chartreuse Massif of the Sub-Alpine Chains. The rock is composed of blocks of Mid-Cretaceous limestone within a matrix of fine-grained gouge.

Fracturing followed by sliding along the fractures generates cavities in the rock, increasing the porosity and consequently the volume. What was originally solid rock becomes a mix of rock and cavities. This increase in volume, known as **dilation**, means that cataclasis is particularly sensitive to confining pressure. As depth increases, the confining pressure will become too great to allow any increase in volume and hence large-scale fracturing will be inhibited.

One consequence of dilation is that pathways for fluid transport are created within the rock. Sedimentary sequences at high crustal levels contain large quantities of fluid; fluid that commonly carries dissolved minerals. This combination of pathways and availability of fluid means that brittle fault zones are frequently sites for the deposition of minerals such as quartz and, in carbonate-dominated sequences such as the French Alps, calcite. This deposition of minerals may cement together the fragments of the cataclasite and leave the fault rock as a more coherent material than we might otherwise expect.

Activity 2.1

Now attempt the video- and Home Kit-based Activity 2.1, looking in more detail at cataclastic rocks and their textures. You should take about 40 minutes to do this Activity.

2.6.2 Pressure solution

⬤ Do any high crustal level structures require a deformation mechanism other than cataclasis for their formation?

⬤ It is hard to imagine how the folds illustrated in Figures 2.7 and 2.16 could develop simply as a consequence of cataclasis. Cataclasis acts heterogeneously, affecting only some parts of the rock mass. To produce smoothly curving folds, we need a mechanism that acts more uniformly throughout the rock.

Such ductile deformation mechanisms generally require elevated temperatures to operate effectively and yet most of the sediments of the Sub-Alpine Chains appear to be unmetamorphosed. Fossils are preserved intact and the mudrocks are very friable, showing little sign of recrystallization.

> **Question 2.7** On the basis of the stratigraphic thicknesses given in Figure 2.8 and assuming a geothermal gradient of $30\,°C\,km^{-1}$, calculate the maximum temperature reached by an Upper Jurassic massive limestone unit overlain by a duplex containing four repetitions of the Cretaceous sequence.

In this temperature range, the original clay minerals in the mudrocks begin to re-order their crystal lattices, but they remain as clay minerals rather than converting to mica. As a consequence, cleavages, if detectable at all, are very poorly developed. Ductile deformation mechanisms that change the shape of mineral grains by distorting their crystal lattices operate so slowly at these temperatures that they are of little practical relevance to rock deformation. The most efficient ductile rock deformation mechanism under these conditions is **pressure solution**, the mass transfer of material by water-assisted diffusion away from areas of high mean stress (Figure 2.27).

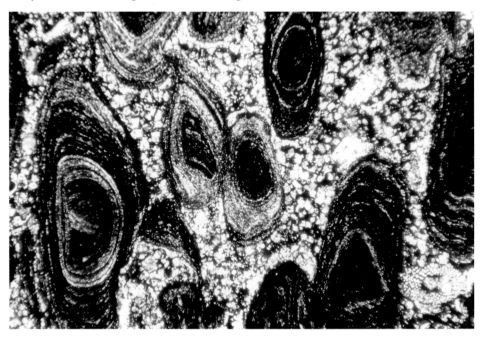

Figure 2.27 Truncation of ooids by pressure solution. Note that an originally circular shape has been modified to an approximate ellipse.

● Which minerals are most susceptible to pressure solution?

● The two minerals that deform most easily by pressure solution are quartz and calcite. As we have noted, the stratigraphy of the Sub-Alpine Chains is dominated by limestone and so the pressure solution of calcite is the most significant deformation process governing the formation of the folds.

Pressure solution requires the presence of a fluid phase along the grain boundaries in order for the dissolved material to be transported away. The upper crustal environment provides such fluids in abundance.

2.7   Summary of Section 2

• Deformation within an orogenic belt can be divided into an Inner Zone and an Outer Zone. The Outer Zone grades into the undeformed foreland. Deformation in the Outer Zone takes place at low temperatures and consequently metamorphic changes are relatively unimportant.

• In the Western Alps, the Outer Zone can be subdivided into mountain ranges composed of deformed cover, the Sub-Alpine Chains, and higher mountains composed of basement, the External Crystalline Massifs.

• The structure of the Sub-Alpine Chains is dominated by thrust faulting and associated fault-related folding. The predominant displacement on the thrusts is towards the west, defining the chains as a foreland thrust belt.

• Thrust systems are characterized by imbrication, leading to the development of duplexes and imbricate fans, and by thrusts cutting across stratigraphy to form ramps. These features can be recognized in three-dimensional views of thrust systems but are most commonly depicted in sections drawn parallel to the direction in which the hanging-wall has moved.

- Faults with different movement directions and their related folds form linked systems of structures that enable large volumes of rock to be deformed. Transfer zones are areas of complex deformation that link individual faults.

- The uplift of the External Crystalline Massifs has, in part, been brought about by thrust faults. These faults are commonly older structures that have been reactivated during the Alpine orogeny.

- Faults move and propagate incrementally in response to stresses that vary over time.

- Cataclasis and pressure solution, acting together at the granular scale, provide the mechanisms by which upper crustal rocks can deform and develop large-scale structures.

Objectives for Section 2

Now that you have completed this Section, you should be able to:

2.1   Understand the meaning of all the terms printed in **bold**.

2.2   Recognize which parts of an orogenic belt have been deformed at upper crustal levels.

2.3   Describe the geometry of the structures formed in a foreland thrust belt and interpret their role in the evolution of an orogen.

2.4   Explain the necessary linkages between structures.

2.5   Recognize the evidence that determines which deformation mechanisms operated during the formation of upper crustal level structures.

Now try the following questions to test your understanding of Section 2.

Question 2.8 How are the Sub-Alpine Chains related to the basement rocks of the External Crystalline Massifs?

Question 2.9 Describe and explain two ways in which folds can develop in association with thrust faulting.

3 Structures produced at deeper levels in the crust

One of the characteristics of structures that form at shallow crustal levels is the virtual absence of metamorphism. As temperature and pressure usually increase smoothly with depth, it would be reasonable to expect that there would be a gradual transition from the high-level structures to ones that are associated with significant degrees of metamorphism. To some extent this is true. Lower Jurassic strata from near the base of the succession in the Col d'Ornon area (Figure 2.23a) show a strong cleavage (Figure 3.1). The growth of muscovite replacing clay minerals is an indication of increasing metamorphic temperatures. However, foreland thrust belts are characterized by a sole thrust that marks a clearly defined base to thrust-related deformation (Figure 2.7). Below this we should not expect to find a continuation of this trend.

Figure 3.1 Spaced cleavage planes in Lower Jurassic limestones and more intensely cleaved interbedded marls, Bourg d'Oisans, French Alps. The cleavage is partly defined by aligned muscovite grains.

⬤ Where should we look for deeper-level rocks that have been affected by the same orogenic events that caused the foreland thrust belt?

⬤ As the thrust belt rocks have been displaced towards the foreland, we should look in the opposite direction, towards the Inner Zone of the orogenic belt.

In the context of the French Alps (Figure 2.4), we should look at the area straddling the border with Italy. In this area, the rocks are highly deformed and metamorphosed although in places a stratigraphy very similar to that of the Sub-Alpine Chains is discernible. The rocks found within the thrust sheets of the Inner Zones include some of the same carbonate-dominated Mesozoic shelf sequences that are found in the Outer Zone but they have been deformed much more intensely.

Question 3.1 The structures illustrated in Figure 3.2 have many points of contrast with those that we have looked at from the Sub-Alpine Chains. Complete Table 3.1 by comparing this Figure to any of the relevant Figures from Section 2.

(a)

(b)

Figure 3.2 (a) Large-scale tight fold of Jurassic limestones, Vallée de la Maurienne, French Alps. (b) Strongly foliated sediments, Italian Alps.

Table 3.1 For use with Question 3.1.

	Folded layer profile shape	Interlimb angle	Axial plane fabric
Sub-Alpine Chains			
Inner Zone thrust sheets			

One very striking feature of the Inner Zone thrust sheets is the presence of large-scale recumbent folds with a single fold often affecting the entire thickness of a thrust sheet. These were called **fold nappes** when they were first recognized and this term is still widely used today to refer to a hanging-wall block of a major thrust that contains large-scale recumbent folds (Figure 3.3). The feature that distinguishes nappes from thrust sheets is the presence of overturned stratigraphy, representing the inverted lower limb of the recumbent fold.

Figure 3.3 The Morcles Nappe, Helvetic Alps, Switzerland.

These features of Inner Zone folds are diagnostic of deformation under higher temperature conditions; they are the products of ductile deformation. Bearing in mind that the Inner Zone and Outer Zone sediments were laid down at the Earth's surface during the same time period, we must now answer the question of why the Inner Zone rocks have been subjected to higher temperatures and pressures.

- What factors could lead to part of the crust experiencing higher temperatures than a neighbouring section?

- Either the particular section of the crust had a higher heat flow, and hence rocks at a given depth would experience a higher temperature, or the rocks had been buried to a deeper level.

We will deal with variations in heat flow in detail later (Section 6) but for the present we can simply state that there is no reason to expect that the heat flow in the Inner Zones was markedly different. The more likely explanation is that the rocks of the Inner Zone have been more deeply buried. Importantly, they must have had to remain at those depths for long enough to achieve the higher temperatures.

What constituted the overlying material that buried these Inner Zone rocks? We already know part of the answer because we have established that the Sub-Alpine Chains were transported north-westwards and so previously could have overlain the Inner Zone rocks. However, this is not the complete answer as you can see by looking back at Figure 2.2. The collision also resulted in the thrust stacking of fragments of both the Tethys oceanic crust and the continental microplate of Italy, on top of the European margin sediments.

The present-day configuration exposes the Inner Zone rocks at the surface, so whatever units were overlying them have now been removed by uplift and erosion. Clearly, not all parts of the Alpine belt have been uplifted at the same rate and we will look in more detail at this aspect of orogeny in Section 7.

3.1   The Caledonian Orogenic Belt in Scotland

Although the Inner Zone of the Alps is well exposed, erosion has not yet had time to reveal all the features of its history. In this Section, we will also draw on examples from a much older orogenic belt, the Caledonian Orogenic Belt (often referred to as the Caledonides) of NW Europe – and, in particular, the Scottish segment of this orogenic belt.

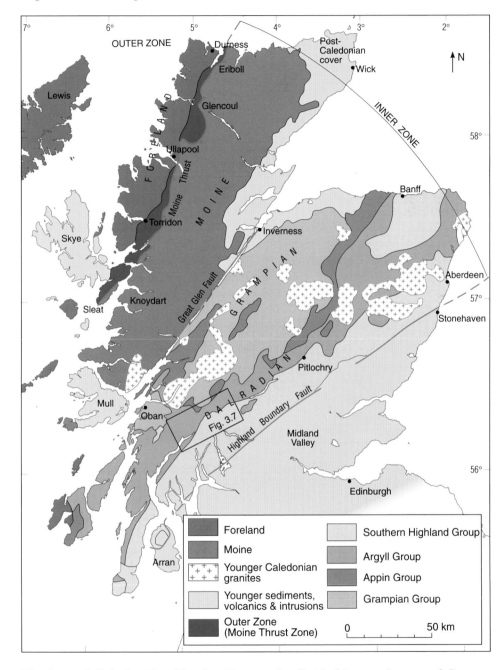

Figure 3.4 Map of Northern Scotland identifying the broad stratigraphic and tectonic divisions within the Caledonian Orogenic Belt.

The Scottish Caledonides, like the Alps, can be divided into an Inner and Outer Zone. The Outer Zone in the Caledonides is exposed in the north-west of Scotland, and is termed the **Moine Thrust Belt** (Figure 3.4). This is comprised of several north-west-directed thrusts that overthrust deeper rocks from the east onto the imbricated foreland rocks (Figure 3.5).

Figure 3.5 The Glencoul thrust. Late Archean–Proterozoic basement (Lewisian gneisses) overthrusting Cambrian quartzites which unconformably overlie the Lewisian basement (Ben Aird da loch).

The foreland is made up of three components. The Lewisian gneisses provide the late Archean–Proterozoic basement which is locally overlain by Proterozoic sediments (the Torridonian Supergroup). The Torridonian sequence provides a good example of layer-cake stratigraphy (Figure 3.6). The third component is a narrow strip of Cambro-Ordovician shelf sediments which unconformably overlie both the Lewisian and Torridonian rocks. The unconformity is planar and dips gently back under the Caledonian mountain belt (to the south-east).

The Inner Zone is largely made up of metamorphosed sediments, known as the Moine succession, exposed between the Moine Thrust Belt and the Great Glen Fault, and the Dalradian and Grampian successions, exposed between the Great Glen Fault and the Highland Boundary Fault (Figure 3.4). We are mainly concerned in this section with the **Dalradian Supergroup**.

The basin into which the Dalradian sediments were deposited is thought to have existed for at least 100 Ma, with sedimentation ceasing during the Cambrian or Early Ordovician. The Dalradian sediments, along with some interbedded basaltic volcanic units, were deposited unconformably on top of a previously deformed and metamorphosed basement, the Grampian Group. During the early evolution of the basin, the continental shelf formed by the Grampian Group was undergoing extension. Normal faults controlled the pattern of Dalradian sedimentation in much the same way as occurred during deposition of the Triassic–Lower Jurassic sequences in the Alps.

Figure 3.6 Layer-cake stratigraphy of Torridonian sandstones on the Caledonian foreland (Suilven).

The Caledonian Orogenic Belt stretches from Scandinavia through northern Britain to the east coast of North America. As geologists have learned more about this tract of land, it has been realized that intermittent deformation has continued from the Cambrian to the Devonian resulting from the rather complex closure of the Iapetus Ocean. Within this lengthy timespan, discrete phases can now be recognized. In Scotland, the Inner Zone was subjected to a series of tectonic events, beginning with extension around 600 Ma and followed by collision at around 470–460 Ma, an event termed (by geologists working in

Scotland) the Grampian phase of the Caledonian Orogeny. A later collision, around 420–400 Ma, is known as the Acadian phase, resulting in widespread deformation of the Northern Appalachians and, in north-west Scotland, the thrust tectonics of the Outer Zone. You need to be aware of potentially confusing terminology here, as some geologists use the term 'Caledonian Orogeny' specifically to refer to this younger event.

Metamorphism during the Grampian phase caused much of the Dalradian to reach garnet grade or higher, with mineral assemblages indicating peak conditions of at least 550 °C and pressures equivalent to depths of 20–25 km. The deformation geometries shown by these rocks are complex, principally because there are several different deformation events superimposed on one another. However, we will soon see that there are some basic rules that we can apply to unravel the geometrical patterns in these rocks and that they tell a fascinating story.

Activity 3.1

You should now attempt the video-based Activity introducing you to the Caledonian orogenic belt in Scotland. You should take about 20 minutes to do this Activity.

3.2   Large-scale Inner Zone structures

We have already seen that the stacking of thrust sheets is a fundamental component of the deformation story in the Inner Zone of the Alps. We should start our more detailed look at structures in the Dalradian by checking to see if thrusts have played a major role here as well.

- What evidence, on maps or cross-sections, should we look for in order to test this hypothesis?

- We need to look for systematic repetitions of the stratigraphy across discontinuities.

We could also suggest that we should look for the classic 'older in the hanging-wall, younger in the footwall' relationship. However, we may not always see this as subsequent deformation events may have folded the thrust planes and obscured the original age relationships.

Look at Figure 3.7a and examine the Upper Glen Lyon area. There are five occurrences of the Grampian Group/Appin Group contact separated by discontinuities that are labelled **slides**. Slides, then, are breaks in the stratigraphy, but are they thrusts?

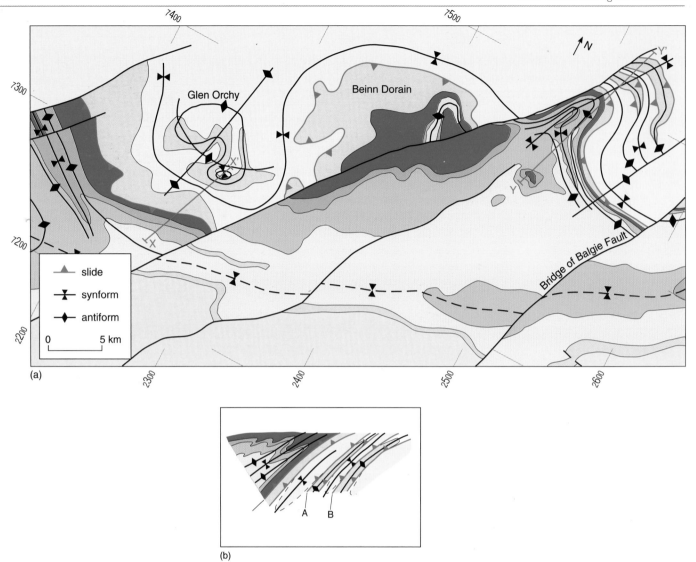

Map colour	Group	Sub-Group	Thickness/km
	Southern Highland		3.4
	Argyll	Tayvallich	2.1
		Crinan	0.8
		Easdale	4.1
		Islay	4.4
	Appin	Blair Atholl	1.5
		Ballachulish	1.4
		Lochaber	4.0
	Grampian		Base not seen

(c)

Figure 3.7 (a) Map of the Glen Lyon and Ben Lui area (located on Figure 3.4). (b) Schematic cross-section showing slide disruption of Dalradian stratigraphy in the area of the Y–Y' line, Glen Lyon. (c) Stratigraphic column for the Ben Lui/Glen Lyon area. The Easdale Sub-Group has been subdivided on the map and cross-sections in order to show details of its folded structure.

Question 3.2 Figure 3.8 shows a schematic cross-section of the Iltay Boundary Slide. In the units below the slide, only the Lochaber Sub-Group of the Appin Group is present. By reference to the stratigraphic column (Figure 3.7c), does the slide have a normal or a reverse sense of movement? What is the total thickness of the stratigraphy that is either missing or repeated across the slide?

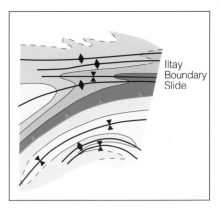

Figure 3.8 Schematic cross-section of the Iltay Boundary Slide in the area of the X–X′ line (Figure 3.7a), Ben Lui.

The slides in Figure 3.7a do not show a consistent age relationship; either older or younger rocks can be in the hanging-wall. However, the cross-section (Figure 3.7b) shows that there is, in fact, only a single slide that has been folded around almost isoclinal folds. Where the slide has been folded and consequently the older rocks are present in the hanging-wall, the structure appears to have a reverse sense of displacement; for example, the slides labelled A and B on Figure 3.7b. The term 'slide' was introduced by geologists mapping the Dalradian because the discontinuities show this complexity of age relationships and the true movement sense is not always immediately apparent. Detailed mapping has shown that many of them do have a normal sense of displacement and so they cannot be simple equivalents of the brittle thrusts of the Outer Zone. Normal faults, though, act as extensional structures and so their presence in this environment needs some clarification.

Question 3.3 What explanations can you suggest for the presence of normal faults in a collision zone where the tectonic framework is dominated by shortening processes?

3.2.1 Early normal faults

When we looked at the higher crustal level structures in the Alps, we were able to identify early normal faults, bounding half-graben basins (see Figure 2.23). Within the cover sequence, it was often possible to see that these faults had acted with a thrust sense of displacement during the shortening events, e.g. the Rencurel thrust. However, look now at another fault on Figure 2.23a, the Col d'Ornon fault. This structure still appears as a normal fault in spite of being reactivated during the shortening events.

- What will govern whether a normal fault, reactivated as a thrust, finally shows a normal or a reverse sense of displacement?

- It simply depends on the relative amounts of normal and reverse movement. Think of normal displacements as negative numbers and reverse as positive. Add all the increments together and if you end up with a positive result, the final structure will map out as a reverse fault; negative, and you are left with a normal fault.

Question 3.4 Figure 3.9 (overleaf) shows three stages in the development of a half-graben. Measure the displacements of the three horizons, A, B and C, at the three stages. Sketch the configuration after the fault has undergone reverse-sense reactivation with 15 m of displacement.

At the end of the normal-sense development of this fault, the lowest horizon had more than double the displacement of the highest one. After reactivation, the structure becomes a hybrid with reverse fault characteristics at its upper levels but remaining as a normal fault at depth.

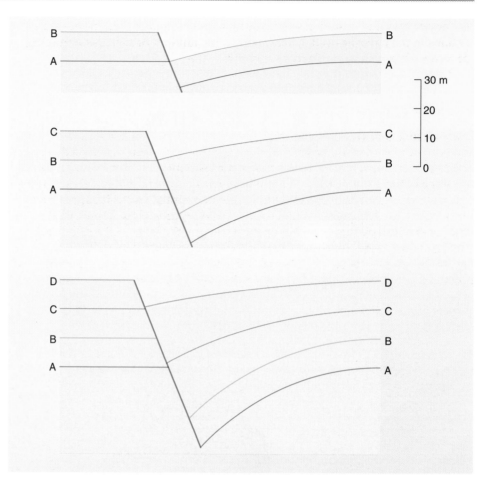

Figure 3.9   Drawing of three stages in the development of a growth fault, for use with Question 3.4.

Many of the Dalradian slides map out as normal faults, suggesting that present-day erosion levels expose rocks near the base of the original half-graben structures. One further test could be applied before accepting this explanation. Can we detect the variations in stratigraphic sequence across the slides that would result if they had originally been growth faults? Figure 3.10 compares the sequence in the hanging-wall and footwall of the Fort William Slide. There is a very thin development of Lochaber Group quartzite in the footwall but this unit is very much thicker and separated into three quartzite units in the hanging-wall. The Dalradian slides, then, do represent highly modified growth faults that originally bounded half-graben. However, because of the major variations in stratigraphic thicknesses that occur across such faults, we should look again at the figure of 7.3 km of missing section that we determined in the answer to Question 3.2. That the succession is missing is undeniable, but if the slide represents a growth fault, some of the units may never have been deposited in

Figure 3.10   Cross-section through the Fort William Slide after the deposition of the Appin Group. The footwall carries only a thin layer of sandy sediments whilst the hanging-wall sequence contains much thicker sand units interbedded with deeper-water, finer-grained sediments. (From R. Anderton (1998) 'Dalradian slides and basin development', *Journal of the Geological Society*, vol. 145, Geological Society Publishing House.)

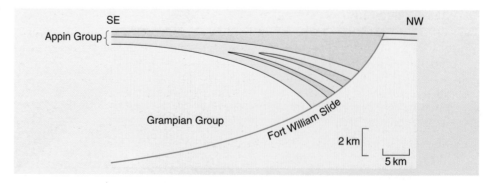

the footwall whilst those that were would be much thinner than the equivalent sections in the hanging-wall. Consequently, the amount of succession missing for tectonic reasons would be considerably less than 7.3 km.

3.2.2 Late normal faults

In answering Question 3.3, you established that normal faults within a collision zone can belong to an early stage in the evolution of the orogen. In contrast, another mechanism for producing major normal faults can come into play at a *late* stage in the growth of a mountain belt. The end result of a collision orogeny is a much-thickened lithosphere with consequent uplift. Uplift is supported by a range of forces acting on the orogen and by the rigidity of the underthrust lithosphere. If there is any change to these factors, the inevitable result is the development of structures that attempt to restore mechanical equilibrium. Figure 3.11 shows the style of normal fault that can help to bring this about in a process that has been referred to, rather dramatically, as **orogenic collapse**.

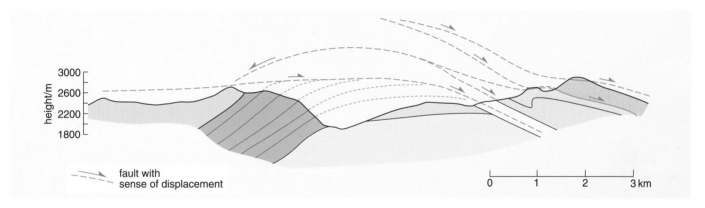

fault with
sense of displacement

3.2.3 The basement-to-cover tectonic transition

Both the Alpine and Dalradian orogens have provided examples of fault reactivation and demonstrated that the basement is intimately involved in the shortening process. It is found as thrust slices within the cover sequence. A general model for the evolution of the basement-cover relationship is shown in Figure 3.12 (overleaf).

Figure 3.11 Cross-section through Upper Val Gresseney, Italian Alps. Flat-lying faults with a normal sense of displacement have caused the thickened post-collision crust to thin by uncovering successively lower tectonic units.

Wherever possible, the deformation will make use of pre-existing basement structures that can propagate up into the cover sequence. However, the extent of the shortening and thickening present in these Inner Zone rocks means that both cover and basement must be able to change their shape dramatically, irrespective of whether structures are available for reactivation. In the Outer Zone, the stratigraphy exerted a major control on the mechanism of shortening, the position of the thrusts being determined by the less competent horizons (see Question 2.2). Basement rocks, on the other hand, have previously been metamorphosed and deformed. This results in there being fewer major competence contrasts between rock types for the deformation to exploit. Initially, the cover sequence does have an exploitable stratigraphy but the multiple deformation events typical of Inner Zone tectonics gradually destroy this. These rocks, too, must adopt other shortening mechanisms in order to continue to react to the stresses set up by the collision.

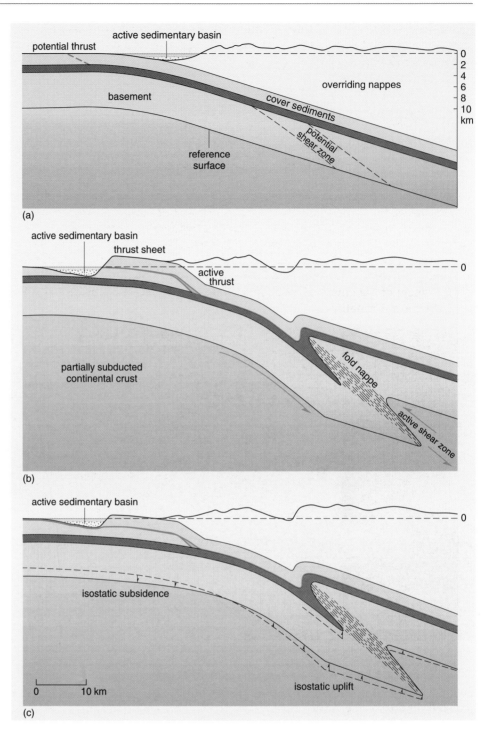

Figure 3.12 Model for the development of structures in the cover and basement during the evolution of a collision zone. Note that all the units shown are of continental crust. Oceanic lithosphere has already been completely subducted.

Outer Zone structures tend to be visible on the large scale (Figure 3.5). Discrete thrusts are readily identified and blocks of stratigraphy tens of kilometres long and perhaps a kilometre thick have been stacked on top of each other by movement along the thrust planes. Deformation is concentrated within and close to these thrusts, away from which the rocks may show little or no sign of folding or cleavage development. By contrast, in the Inner Zone deformation is pervasive; it affects the rocks at all scales down to that of individual mineral grains. As a consequence, to discover the mechanisms by which the Inner Zone rocks have accommodated the necessary shortening, we must look at features on a much smaller scale. Remember, the structures we see on the metre or ten-metre scale, when repeated throughout the rocks of the Inner Zone, have a dramatic effect on the dimensions of the crust, equal to the more striking thrusts of the Outer Zone.

3.3 Shear zones

On the scale of a cross-section such as Figure 3.8, we can only use single lines to depict the slides. However, when examined in outcrop, we find not a discrete planar surface but rather a zone of deformed rocks such as shown in Figure 3.13. These zones can be tens of metres across and consist of strongly foliated, fine-grained rocks. Such zones are the ductile equivalent of faults and are termed **shear zones**. Across these zones, there can be considerable displacement of the hanging-wall with respect to the footwall but usually there is no identifiable surface along which frictional sliding could have taken place. Rather, the fine-grained rocks represent a highly deformed zone within which the relative displacement of hanging-wall and footwall has accumulated by means of grain-scale ductile deformation.

Figure 3.13 Highly sheared Grampian Group rocks from the Fort William Slide, North shore, Loch Leven.

In this Section, we will first establish the shape and configuration of shear zones and then return to the vitally important role that they play in changing the shape of ductile rock masses.

3.3.1 Shear zone geometry

In order to understand shear zones, it is useful to start by describing an ideal, simplified model and then refine this by looking at natural examples. John Ramsay and Rod Graham, then at Imperial College London, first described the ideal shear zone in a 1970 paper in which they developed the basic geometrical rules.

Figure 3.14 shows that their ideal shear zone has parallel planar sides. Beyond these bounding surfaces, the deformation that generated the shear zone caused no change in shape of the rock mass. So a measure of deformation intensity, such as the shear strain γ, is zero outside the boundaries of the zone and increases towards the centre as depicted on the graph. A shear zone is fundamentally a zone of heterogeneous deformation. It exists because the deformation is localized into bands within the rock mass, and within each band the deformation intensity varies systematically from one side to the other.

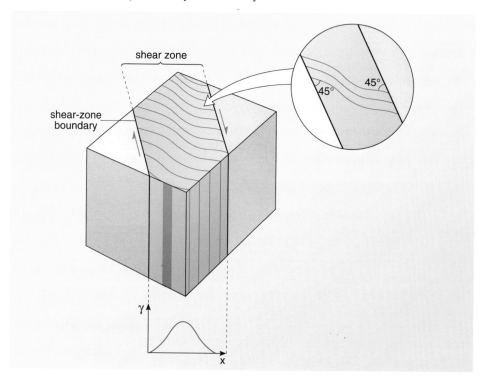

Figure 3.14 Block view of a simple shear zone with planar sides and a foliation developed within the boundaries of the zone. The graph shows the variation of shear strain (γ) against distance (x) measured across the zone. The foliation makes an angle of 45° with the edges of the zone but, as the shear strain increases, the foliation rotates towards parallelism with the zone boundaries.

In its simplest form, the ideal shear zone has exactly the pattern of deformation you would expect if it had deformed like a stack of cards being pushed from the side. Figure 3.15a shows such a card stack that can be deformed by pressing a template to the edge of the cards. The intensity of the deformation is measured by the angle ψ, the tangent of which, γ, is the measure of shear strain. This pattern of deformation is known as **simple shear**. In Figure 3.15b (top), the value of γ is the same at every point across the model because the template has a constant angle, ψ. This is an example of homogeneous simple shear, but we need to consider the case where the shear intensity varies across the zone and this is illustrated by a heterogeneous simple shear zone in Figure 3.15b (bottom).

We can use the card stack analogy to identify two very important directions. There must be a **shear plane**, oriented parallel to the surface of the cards, and a **shear direction**, the direction in which each card has moved relative to its neighbour. The shear plane should be parallel to the boundaries of the zone and the shear direction must be constrained to be a line that lies on the shear plane rather than cutting across it.

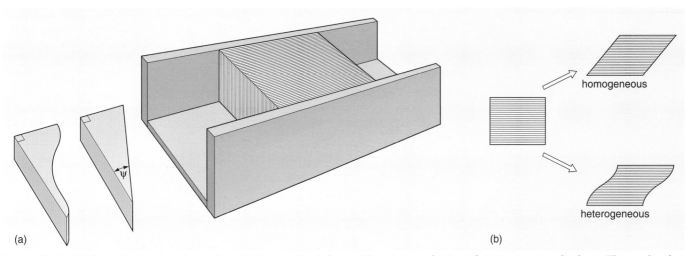

Figure 3.15 (a) Shear box with a stack of cards that can be deformed by a triangular template to give simple shear. The angle of the template, ψ, is the angular shear strain, the tangent of which is γ, the shear strain. (b) Shape of card stack after deformation by homogeneous simple shear (top) and deformation with a curved template to give heterogeneous simple shear (bottom).

Question 3.5 What structural feature of the shear zone in Figure 3.13 is likely to correspond to the shear plane?

This can be verified by looking at a small-scale example of a shear zone where the bounding surfaces of the zone can readily be identified (Figure 3.16). Here, the foliation is only developed within the shear zone and its intensity increases towards its centre. The foliation is oriented sub-parallel to the zone sides in the highest strain area at the centre whilst in the lower strain areas, towards the edges of the zone, it makes an increasingly high angle with the sides. This produces the sigmoidal pattern of foliation trace that is the most readily identified feature of small-scale shear zones. Often we can identify similar changes in the orientation of features at map scale and thus pick out much larger shear zones (Figure 3.17).

Figure 3.16 Shear zone in basement gneisses, Kola Peninsula, Russia. Grains are elongated and define a sigmoidal, curving foliation within the shear zone. Grains are equidimensional outside the planar boundaries of the zone.

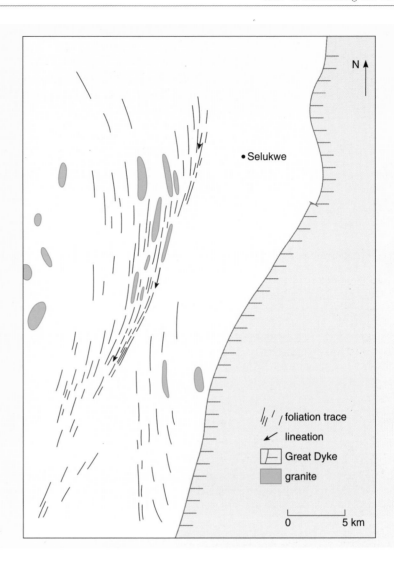

Figure 3.17 Map scale shear zone (Selukwe greenstone belt, Zimbabwe).

Question 3.6 What is the trend (orientation with respect to north) of the boundaries of the Selukwe shear zone (Figure 3.17)? What is the approximate width of the shear zone?

Figure 3.18 Lineation of stretched calcite grains on a foliation surface, Rocher de l'Yret, French Alps.

If we look at a foliation surface from the high strain centre of a shear zone (Figure 3.18), we can see a set of lines or lineation. In this example, the lineation turns out to be defined by elongated calcite grains and these appear as light streaks in the photograph. The lines mark the direction in which the rock has been stretched by the greatest amount. This **mineral stretching lineation** corresponds to the shear direction defined earlier.

If the foliation plane and mineral stretching lineation are identified within a shear zone, then it is possible to deduce the relative movement direction of the hanging-wall and footwall blocks. This is a vitally important conclusion that we return to in the next Section.

So far, we have discussed the geometry of an ideal shear zone but such a simple model has two limitations as an analogy for a real shear zone. The first is that no matter how far one side of the zone is displaced with respect to the other, the distance between the two sides has to remain the same. Think back to the card stack analogy. If we start with a pack of 100 cards, the thickness of 100 cards then determines the distance between the top and bottom (i.e. the width of the shear zone). No matter how far we slide the cards, there are still 100 cards in the stack and so the top and bottom stay the same distance apart. With this analogue model, a limit is reached: when the displacement exceeds the length of the card, the model falls apart, literally! In a natural shear zone, deforming to this pattern, there are no such artificial limits. Theoretically, we could accumulate any amount of strain, and the width of the zone would stay the same. Another way of expressing this condition is to say that the volume of the affected rock would have to stay the same.

The second limitation is that the ideal shear zone can extend indefinitely. In reality, shear zones have finite length and link together with transfer zones in similar ways to faults. Shear zones are the ductile equivalents of faults and similar principles govern their behaviour.

These limitations serve to illustrate an important principle. As is so often the case, it is useful to build up an understanding of a complex phenomenon using a model that is based on a few simple rules. One of the keys to successful science is to recognize when the limits of a working model have been reached. Further progress is then made by modifying the model, not the observations!

3.3.2 Shear zone terminations

Shear zone terminations can best be illustrated by looking at what actually happens at the ends of shear zones. As the shear zone propagates, the shear zone tip line, exactly analogous to a fault tip line, will be surrounded by a region of more diffuse ductile strains, accommodating the reduction in displacement on the shear zone itself (Figure 3.19a). This ductilely deformed region will eventually come into contact with an equivalent region belonging to a neighbouring shear zone (Figure 3.19b). At this point, further propagation of either zone will be inhibited by the interference between their tips. The result is that the shear zones curve towards each other and eventually coalesce (Figure 3.19c). This can occur on any scale of shear zone but when it is repeated in large numbers of small shear zones it produces the classic curving and branching foliation patterns found in sheared rocks (Figure 3.19d), known as an anastomosing shear fabric.

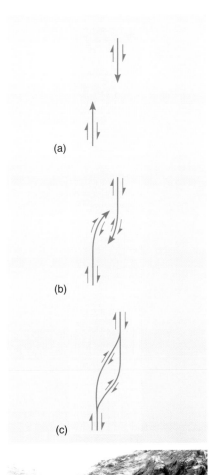

(a)

(b)

(c)

(d)

Figure 3.19 (a) Two shear zones propagate towards each other. (b) Shear zones curve towards each other as they interfere with each other's propagation. (c) Shear zones have merged to leave a shear-bounded lens of material. (d) Anastomosing shear fabric (Phillips Point, Cornwall).

3.3.3 Shear zone fabrics

We should now turn our attention to what happens at the grain scale in order to allow shear zones to develop and deform rock in the manner we have described. There are two processes that allow rocks to deform without causing fractures to develop: pressure solution, which has already been described (Section 2.6.2) and **crystal plastic deformation**.

Crystal plasticity refers to the range of deformation mechanisms that rely on the existence of defects in the crystal structure of all naturally occurring minerals. These defects, termed dislocations, are the result of either incorrectly positioned or missing atoms in the crystal lattice. When a grain is stressed, the defects can move through the lattice, generating new defects. The defects will eventually link and assemble to create more substantial areas of non-standard crystal lattice. Such processes are temperature dependent; they operate more efficiently at higher temperatures and eventually break down as the rock begins to melt.

Pressure solution operates at relatively low temperatures providing a fluid is present. Pressure solution continues to operate as the temperature increases but a point is reached where crystal plastic processes operate more quickly and therefore begin to dominate the deformation. This interplay between deformation mechanisms constantly affects natural rock deformation. As the parameters that control deformation mechanisms, such as temperature, pressure, strain rate and fluid composition, change, so the different mechanisms inter-relate in different ways, giving rise to an enormous variety of structural geometries.

● Figure 3.20 consists of two photomicrographs (a and b) showing the same lithology from outside and within a shear zone. List two differences between the photographs.

● (i) The grain size is much reduced in the sample from within the shear zone. (ii) The quartz grains have become elongated, frequently to the extent that they can be referred to as quartz ribbons.

These differences are all due to the operation of crystal plastic deformation. As the production of a foliation is a frequent consequence of deformation, point (ii) should not come as any surprise. But why should the deformation be accompanied by a reduction in grain size?

(a)

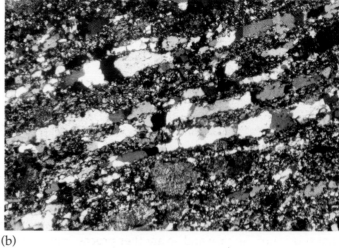
(b)

Figure 3.20 (a) Undeformed and (b) deformed samples of metagranite from a shear zone, seen between crossed polars. Width of images 3 mm.

Figure 3.21 shows what can happen as the lattice defects responsible for crystal plastic deformation increase in density and become organized. They form narrow bands that separate areas where the lattice has a different orientation.

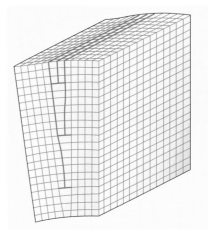

When looking down a microscope with crossed polars at an aggregate of quartz grains, how can we tell where one grain ends and another begins?

There may be a dark line representing the impurities that often collect along grain boundaries, but in the absence of such a feature the form of the grains can only be seen because they have a different orientation of their crystal lattices. A difference in orientation means that the grains go into extinction at different positions as the microscope stage is rotated and we would thus perceive them as distinct grains.

Figure 3.21 Stacking of dislocations into a sub-grain wall, separating areas of crystal lattice with slightly different orientations.

Look again at Figure 3.21 and note that the stacked dislocations are separating areas of different lattice orientation. In effect they are acting as grain boundaries. The process of assembling these stacks of dislocations is a gradual one and initially the angular discordance across the dislocation wall is very small. When it is less than 5 degrees, the features are usually referred to as **sub-grains** but as the process continues the boundaries become better established and a point is reached when it is no longer possible to recognize the original or **host grain**. At this point the new, smaller grains will act independently and be candidates for further deformation. The first sign of this process in quartz is the wavy or undulose extinction that is commonly seen in quartz from metamorphic rocks when viewed under crossed polars. The stages of this process, usually referred to as **dynamic recrystallization**, are illustrated in Figure 3.22.

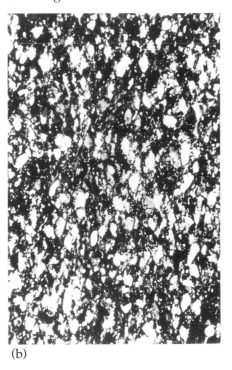
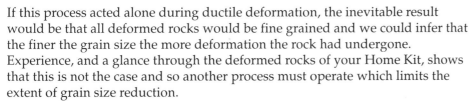

(a)   (b)

Figure 3.22 Stages of quartz deformation from (a) undulose extinction to (b) reduced grain size aggregate. Seen between crossed polars; width of images = 3.5 mm.

If this process acted alone during ductile deformation, the inevitable result would be that all deformed rocks would be fine grained and we could infer that the finer the grain size the more deformation the rock had undergone. Experience, and a glance through the deformed rocks of your Home Kit, shows that this is not the case and so another process must operate which limits the extent of grain size reduction.

This process is **secondary recrystallization** and it doesn't just act to limit the reduction in grain size, but will, in the right circumstances, reverse it. Strained grains, those that have a high density of lattice defects, store a large amount of

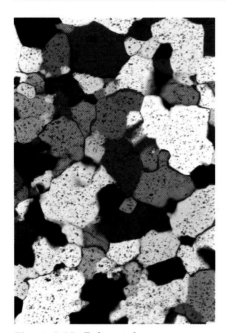

Figure 3.23 Polygonal, equidimensional network of annealed quartz grains. Seen between crossed polars, width of image = 6.5 mm.

energy in their lattice and this energy can be released by the growth of new, strain-free grains. If this process occurs after deformation has ceased, driven by continuing high temperatures, it is referred to as **annealing** and results in a roughly equidimensional, polygonal grain structure such as shown in Figure 3.23.

However, it is more usual for the two processes to be acting simultaneously and in competition with one another. Existing grains will be divided into sub-grains and new grains will grow to incorporate the sub-grains in a cyclical process. The texture that is preserved, i.e. the **microstructure**, will simply be the last 'freeze-frame' from this loop.

Figure 3.24 shows the stress variations that exist during deformation of this type. Strain accumulates during a gradual build up of stress but a steady state may develop during which the deformation can continue without any further increase in stress. At this point, the microstructure will be continuously passing through the stages of the loop described above. Many thousands of cycles can be completed and very large strains will accumulate. A material that continues to deform in response to a steady stress level is what we normally think of as a fluid, and rock exhibiting this behaviour is flowing, albeit very slowly. The graph also shows that this flow may continue even after a stress drop has taken place, behaviour described as **strain softening**. The deformed rock within the shear zone, because of its reduced grain size, is now significantly weaker than the surrounding rock and so will continue to deform preferentially, ensuring that the deformation remains localized within the shear zone.

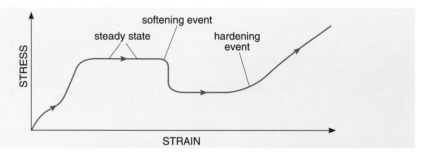

Figure 3.24 Relationship between stress and strain during crystal plastic deformation. This is a one-way path because the strain will not be recovered when stress is removed. This pathway is only one from an infinite variety of possibilities.

We have already established that shear zones are areas of higher deformation compared to the surrounding rock. Therefore, it is not surprising that shear zone rocks are typified by finer grain sizes compared to the lithologies from which they are derived. Rocks that exhibit these characteristics of fine grain size and well-developed foliation, defined by strongly elongate grains, are termed **mylonites**. We can compare and contrast mylonitic fault rocks, as products of ductile deformation, with the cataclastic fault rocks discussed earlier. Whilst they both represent the modification to lithology that results from high intensity shear deformation and both are characterized by a grain size reduction, they are the products of very different deformation mechanisms and therefore have characteristically different microstructures.

Activity 3.2

Now attempt the video- and Home Kit-based Activity 3.2, looking in more detail at mylonites and their textures. You should take about one hour to do this Activity.

Box 3.1 Fold terminology

The terms anticline and syncline are commonly used to describe fold shapes, but these terms imply a knowledge of the relative ages of the rock units which are folded. An anticline is defined as a fold that has the oldest units exposed in the centre or core of the structure and a syncline as one where the youngest units are in the core. However, in mylonites, and many other metamorphic rocks, the folded fabric is tectonic rather than stratigraphic layering. In this case there is no sense of relative age associated with such a fabric. Even when the folds are of bedding, the deformation may have been so intense that it has made it impossible to determine the relative ages of the units.

The terms **antiform** and **synform** overcome this problem and are illustrated in Figure 3.25. These terms are based on the idea of a **closing direction**. In order to assess the closing direction of a fold, we need to look at a *normal profile section,* that is one perpendicular to the fold axis. We then determine the direction, *along the trace of the axial plane,* in which the limbs of the fold come together, or *close.* A fold with an upwards closing direction is an antiform and one with a downwards closing direction is a synform.

There does remain the possibility that a fold could close precisely sideways, neither up nor down. This is described as a **neutral fold**.

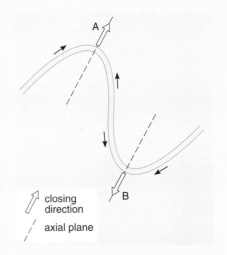

Figure 3.25 The closing direction of a fold is the direction traced along the axial plane in which the limbs come together. A is an antiform closing upwards, B is a synform closing downwards

3.3.4 Shear zone folds

During the development of a ductile shear zone, the rock is effectively flowing and this results in a distinct mechanism for developing folds.

Question 3.7 Figure 3.26 shows folding of the planar fabric of a mylonite. Describe the fold shape, noting any variations of (i) the thickness of the layers as they pass around the fold and (ii) the fold shape from layer to layer.

Figure 3.26 Fold developed within sheared gneisses, Kola Peninsula, Russia. The photograph is taken looking towards the SE.

Such fold shapes cannot be the result of simple shortening parallel to the layers. If you tried to unfold the layers in Figure 3.26 by laying a piece of string along them and then pulling it taut, you would come up with an enormous variation in 'undeformed' lengths. These folds are shear, or flow, folds and form by a quite different process.

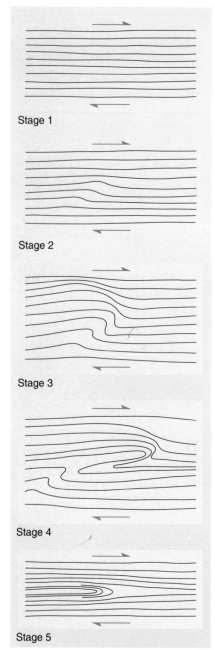

Stage 1

Stage 2

Stage 3

Stage 4

Stage 5

Figure 3.27 Stages in the development of a shear fold. The fold grows in size from an initial perturbation of the foliation and becomes progressively more asymmetric. Eventually, the axial plane of the fold becomes parallel to the foliation and the fold is effectively re-absorbed into the plane of the foliation.

The simplest flow pattern adopted by fluids is laminar flow, when all points in the fluid move in parallel lines in the direction of the current. Frequently, though, internal currents may be set up which cause individual points in the fluid to move downstream with a much more complex path. This is called turbulent flow. In order to be able to see the effects of these different types of flow, some form of marker is needed. In a river, trails of bubbles often reveal the detailed directions of flow and they trace out short-lived swirls which affect small areas of the water, first developing and then being destroyed as the flow progresses. In flowing rock, the mylonitic foliation fulfils the same role as the bubbles. The folds are marking the patches of turbulent flow, albeit in a solid rather than liquid material. The swirls of bubbles in the river are transient features and we must think of folds within shear zones in the same way. There is a significant difference, though, between the flowing water analogy and rock deformation. When flow in the shear zone stopped, the folds that then existed were preserved, representing all stages of their development. By studying the range of preserved fold shapes, we can effectively chart the progression that would have been followed by any one fold during its growth and destruction. Figure 3.27 shows the various stages that such folds must pass through during their evolution.

So far, we have looked at these folds in two dimensions only. In effect, we have looked at the evolution of their cross-sectional profiles, and have only considered sections that are parallel, or close to parallel, to the movement direction. When the view is expanded to encompass the third dimension, shear folds can display some remarkable shapes.

Theoretically, a fold could maintain a constant profile shape in the third dimension along a straight-line axis. Such a simple geometry requires that there is no variation in the shear along that third dimension. Given that shear zones are characterized by heterogeneous shear in their cross-section view (Figure 3.16), such a constraint is unrealistic. We now need to visualize the appearance of folds that were able to respond to variations in the shear intensity along the length of their axes.

A sliding tablecloth over a smooth tabletop provides a simple analogue, illustrating some possible styles of folding. Figure 3.28 shows the elements of the tabletop shear zone in sectional view. The table represents one wall of a horizontal shear zone, the hand represents the other wall and the cloth is the material which is sheared within the zone.

Figure 3.28 Tabletop shear zone. The cloth is pinned along one edge by the cruet set. Movement of the hand rucks up the tablecloth into folds with irregularly curving hinges.

Question 3.8 Try to reproduce the tabletop shear zone shown in Figure 3.28. Anchor one edge of the tablecloth, so that the whole sheet does not move across the table, and place a hand on the other edge. Gently slide your hand towards the anchored edge. Describe the size, amplitude and axis orientation of the folds produced.

The process of sliding one hand over the table (Figure 3.28) is one that has some similarities to a shear zone. The parts of the cloth directly in front of your hand move further forwards than the rest of the cloth and the resulting fold axes have to curve in order to reflect this. This concept of parts of a sliding sheet moving further than other parts has been described in Section 2.2.4 where strike–slip faults partitioned the deformation in thrust sheets. Folds that form in shear zones are the ductile equivalent to this. The upper wall of a flat-lying shear zone is effectively a thrust sheet moving by ductile mechanisms rather than frictional sliding. The deformation, instead of being partitioned by faults, varies smoothly in intensity across the lateral extent of the shear zone.

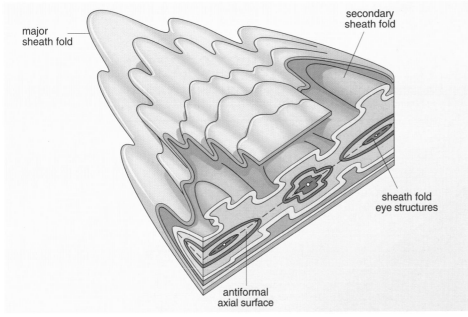

Figure 3.29 Three-dimensional sketch of a major antiformal sheath fold with minor sheath folds on each limb. Note the closed outcrop patterns on the sides of the block.

There is a limit to the amount of curvature a fold axis in a tablecloth can achieve, but in the highly ductile environment of a shear zone there are no such restrictions. Figure 3.29 illustrates the fold shapes that can result from three-dimensional heterogeneous shear. Folds which show extreme hinge curvature, often approaching 180°, are termed **sheath folds** (Figure 3.30) and these tube-like shapes are one of the most dramatic illustrations of the extreme ductility which rocks can

Figure 3.30 A sheath fold in an early stage of its development. The axis curves by approximately 80°, plunging down in the direction of the pencil at the right-hand side of the outcrop (point A) and plunging about 10° in the opposite direction at point B. Kola Peninsula, Russia.

achieve. When a section through a sheath fold is exposed on a flat surface, an outcrop pattern results that is closed in the sense that it is possible to trace each layer around a complete loop. This is shown on the side of the block in Figure 3.29.

Many of the examples featured in this Section have been concerned with small-scale features, so that the complete geometry could be visualized. However, the Selukwe shear zone (Figure 3.17) demonstrates that the geometry can exist at very large scales as well. This also applies to the case of shear zone related folds; they are certainly not confined to the outcrop scale. The fold nappes described earlier (Figure 3.3) are, in many respects, the largest scale examples of shear zone folds, which you can confirm by comparing the fold profile shown in Figure 3.3 with those shown on the left side of the block diagram in Figure 3.29.

3.4 Ductile deformation outside shear zones

Whilst we have stressed that ductile shear zones are important features of deformation at depth, they are by no means the only structures formed there. The slides of the Central Highlands of Scotland (Figure 3.7) are shear zones that occupy only a small proportion of the total area of the Inner Zone. Away from these high strain zones, folds, on a variety of scales, are the dominant structures.

> **Question 3.9** Figure 3.31 shows typical folds in regionally metamorphosed schists. Describe the fold shape, noting any variations in the thickness of the layers as they pass around the fold, and in the fold shape from layer to layer.

Figure 3.31 Folded metasediments. Both bedding and a tectonic fabric are folded around the closure. Kola Peninsula, Russia. Lens cap is 5 cm diameter.

Folds of this style form when a layered sequence is shortened along the length of the layers. They are generally referred to as buckle folds. The direction of maximum shortening is perpendicular to the axial plane of the folds and a planar fabric commonly develops parallel to the axial plane.

3.4.1 Planar fabrics

Intense planar fabrics can develop in shear zones by the process of mylonitization. However, mylonites represent one end member of a spectrum of ductilely deformed rocks. In mylonites, the processes of grain size reduction are dominant, whilst at the other end of the spectrum thoroughly annealed textures are found in many high-grade gneisses. In between lie the majority of deformed and regionally metamorphosed slates and schists. All such rocks possess planar tectonic fabrics that are not necessarily mylonitic.

- Name the two most commonly developed planar tectonic fabrics in regionally metamorphosed rocks.

- They are cleavage and schistosity. The term cleavage is used when it is not possible to see the grains that define the fabric with the naked eye. Rocks that possess such fabrics are called slates. Schistosity, not surprisingly, is applied to schists and is used when the fabric is defined by visible grains.

Planar fabrics are defined by a preferred alignment of mineral grains. The best-developed preferred alignments are found in rocks that are rich in platy grains such as micas. The shape of these grains makes them ideal for defining planes. In the case of other minerals, for example quartz, deformation must flatten the original, roughly equidimensional grains before they can define a set of planes. This process takes longer and requires a higher intensity of deformation, but once achieved, the fabrics will be more stable.

3.4.2 Linear fabrics

Alongside planar fabrics it is often possible to find lineations associated with folds in metamorphic rocks. Figure 3.32 shows elongate pebbles visible in the side view of the outcrop, whilst on the top there is little visible fabric. This observation implies that the pebbles have an elongate rather than a flattened shape. If you find this difficult to envisage, take ten or so pencils and hold them in a bunch. Look at them at any direction except end-on and there is a linear pattern, but end-on the cross-sections show no preferred orientation.

Figure 3.32 Lineated conglomerate. The linear fabric can be seen along the sides of the exposure, but the pebbles are equidimensional on the top surface, showing them to be lines rather than planes. Lens cap is 5 cm diameter.

In order to show such a fabric, the grains in the rock must have been deformed into elongate shapes. Such a lineation is called a **mineral elongation lineation** and whilst quartz grains, for example, need to be deformed into the appropriate shape, other minerals, such as amphiboles, adopt a linear fabric much more readily since their undeformed shape is elongate.

The lineations discussed so far are due to the presence of elongate grains, aligned preferentially in a particular direction. However, lines can be created on the surface of deformed rocks by other mechanisms. One of the most common, but also one of the most misleading, is termed an **intersection lineation**. Intersection lineations are all around us because wherever two planes cross each other a line is visible. The top and side surfaces of a tabletop meet along an edge and if the surfaces are planar the edge is a straight line. Perhaps more analogous to the situation in rocks are the pages of a book. The pages are planar but when we look at the edge of the closed book all we see are the lines that mark the edges of the planes. There will be a similar set of intersection lines produced whenever a set of planes, for example a finely spaced cleavage, intersects a rock face.

It is important to distinguish between a true mineral elongation lineation and an intersection lineation produced by looking edge-on at a set of foliation planes. Figure 3.33 shows the differences; the trick is to find the one unique viewing direction in which the lineation is not visible. Unfortunately, nature does not always provide us with that view and so structural geologists may have to resort to dissecting samples along perpendicular planes.

Intersection lineations are not all bad news, though. Figure 3.34 shows a folded bedding surface intersected by a number of foliation planes. The lineation produced is parallel to the axis of the fold. We would call this feature a **cleavage-bedding intersection lineation**. These lineations are parallel not only to each other, but also to the fold axis. This is important because, once recognized, cleavage-bedding intersection lineations show the orientation of the fold axes in an area, even if the fold closures themselves are not exposed.

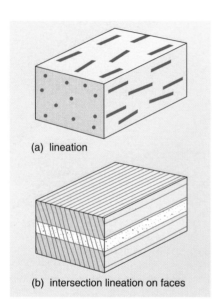

(a) lineation

(b) intersection lineation on faces

Figure 3.33 Block diagrams illustrating (a) mineral elongation lineation and (b) intersection lineation.

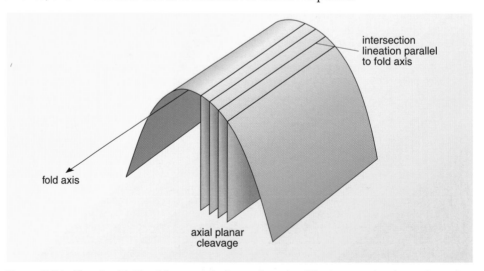

intersection
lineation parallel
to fold axis

fold axis

axial planar
cleavage

Figure 3.34 Sketch of fold with an axial planar cleavage. The intersection line where the cleavage cuts the bedding is parallel to the fold axis.

Activity 3.3

Now attempt Activity 3.3, exploring the relationship between tectonic fabrics and the directions of principal strain. You should take about 90 minutes to do this Activity.

Before leaving this Section, we should emphasize that ductile deformation is of fundamental importance to crustal deformation and mountain building. At the start of Section 3 the term 'thin-skinned' was used to describe the tectonics of the Outer Zone. Such structures typically affect no more than the upper 5 km of the crust. In contrast, Inner Zone rocks of the Caledonides have metamorphic mineral assemblages that place them at 25 km depth for part of their tectonic history. Most of the thickened crust in orogenic belts has been shortened and thickened by ductile structures, such as shear zones and folds, that we have described in this Section.

3.4   Summary of Section 3

- The Inner Zones of orogenic belts were deformed at deeper levels in the crust than the Outer Zones. They are characterized by fold nappes and ductile shear zones.

- The Central Highlands of Scotland are composed of the Dalradian Supergroup sediments deposited unconformably on the Grampian Group basement. Both successions were deformed and metamorphosed during the Grampian phase of the orogeny, between 470 and 460 Ma ago.

- Shear zones are a vital component of Inner Zone deformation. They provide the mechanism by which fold nappes can be emplaced.

- Shear zones are bands of heterogeneous shear deformation that represent the ductile equivalent of faults.

- The highly deformed mylonites within shear zones are strongly foliated and have a reduced grain size. These characteristics are brought about by crystal plastic deformation processes acting at the grain scale.

- Folds formed within shear zones show variable shapes that are related to the flow of rock within the zone. They commonly have strongly curving hinges and are then termed sheath folds.

- Outside of shear zones, buckle folds are the dominant structures. They are associated with the generation of planar and linear tectonic fabrics.

Objectives for Section 3

Now that you have completed this Section, you should be able to:

3.1   Understand the meaning of all the terms printed in **bold**.

3.2   Recognize the styles of structures characteristic of the Inner Zone of an orogenic belt.

3.3   Identify the features typical of a shear zone at a range of scales from individual grains to kilometre-scale fold nappes.

3.4   Describe and explain the sequence of fold shapes typical of shear zones.

3.5   Differentiate between the fold styles generated within and outside of shear zones.

3.6   Identify and explain the significance of planar and linear tectonic fabrics generated within and outside of shear zones.

Now try the following questions to test your understanding of Section 3.

Question 3.10   List the characteristic differences between a thrust sheet from a foreland thrust belt and a fold nappe from the Inner Zone of an orogenic belt.

Question 3.11   Summarize the processes by which mylonites undergo grain size reduction.

Question 3.12   Describe the role that shear zones play in deforming the crust of the Inner Zone.

4 Using structures — kinematics

Recognition of structures from the various parts of an orogenic belt is just a first step towards interpreting their significance for mountain building. We now turn our attention to using these structures to help unravel the history of orogenic belts. There are two strands to this. First, we need to know how the various components of the belt changed their relative positions over time. So we need to study the **kinematics** (from the Greek for motion, *kinema*) of structures in order to deduce the movement of rocks in response to the stresses set up by collision. Secondly, we need to know the sequence of events that brought this about — the **structural chronology**. Understanding the deformation alone will not allow us to establish a complete chronology but structures do provide a vital piece of the jigsaw.

4.1 Fault kinematics

The structures of the Outer Zone are dominated by large thrust faults and these faults present us with clear evidence that blocks of crustal material have moved significant distances relative to one another. In the case of the Alps, we have already studied these structures to deduce that the rocks of the Outer Zone originally made up part of the cover of the External Crystalline Massifs (Figure 2.4). In this Section, we will review the evidence that justifies such deductions.

Marker horizons that can be located in both the hanging-wall and footwall of thrusts, for example the Jurassic/Cretaceous boundary on Figure 2.7, provide the most obvious evidence for the direction and magnitude of displacement. It would be useful, though, if we could infer the movement directions on faults even in the absence of such direct evidence.

4.1.1 Evidence from cataclasites

Question 4.1 What are the lines on the fault plane shown in Figure 4.1? What information do they provide regarding the direction of fault movement?

Figure 4.1 View of a fault surface, for use with Question 4.1.

Just as useful as slickensides are clusters of mineral fibres growing along fault planes, sometimes called slickenfibres. These, too, mark the direction of relative displacement of the faulted blocks (Figure 4.2). It is important to remember that this type of evidence only gives us the direction of movement, not its sense. So, for example, in the case of a fault where the slickensides show that movement was predominantly dip-slip, it is not possible to tell if the fault has normal or reverse movement sense.

Figure 4.2   View of fault plane with fibrous growth of calcite.

There is a further limitation on the usefulness of slickensides and slickenfibres. We have seen that faults develop over time, accumulating displacement in small increments. The slickensides that are preserved only relate to the last, or at best, last few, increments of movement. Frictional sliding on the fault plane destroys such delicate structures and so later increments wipe out the record of earlier movements. This would not be a problem if we could be certain that all the increments of movement on a fault displaced the walls in exactly the same direction. However, this is often not the case. The displacement that is recorded by the offset of any markers will be the vector sum of all the increments (Figure 4.3) and this may not be the same direction as the most recent increment as recorded by the slickensides.

Useful as the evidence of slickensides may be, it only provides a small part of the story. However, this has highlighted again the incremental growth of structures and we shall return to this theme as we build up our understanding of progressive deformation.

The internal structure of cataclasites provides other features which we can use to infer displacement patterns. Figure 4.4 shows a cataclasite from the footwall of a thrust fault. The arrows highlight minor faults that fragment coherent bands within the fault rock, consistently displacing the fragments with a top-to-the-left, or sinistral, shear sense. We can relate such patterns of shear surfaces to the local stress field acting within the fault zone.

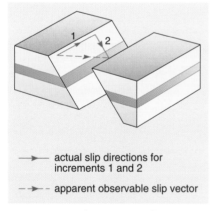

—→— actual slip directions for
        increments 1 and 2

-→-- apparent observable slip vector

Figure 4.3   The concept of a vector sum applied to increments of displacement on a fault. The apparent slip vector will be observable provided that suitable displaced markers exist in the hanging-wall and footwall.

Figure 4.4 Deformation features in the footwall of a thrust.

The stress field within a fault zone will depend on the shearing sense across it, as shown in Figure 4.5, and the subsidiary fractures that form in response to the stresses can be related to that shear sense. When fully developed, the fractures form a conjugate set known as **Riedel shears (R-shears)** that can be used to indicate the overall sense of shear across the fault zone.

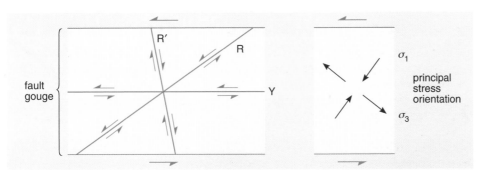

Figure 4.5 Minor fracture (riedel shear) patterns formed in a fault zone and their relationship to the stress field generated by movement on the fault. Note that the principal R-shears have the same shear sense as the main fault and develop at moderate angles to the fault zone walls. The R′-shears develop at high angles and with the opposite shear sense. The Y-shears are simply zones of concentrated fault displacements, parallel to the main fault zone. σ_1 is the maximum principal compressive stress and σ_3 is the minimum principal compressive stress. The intermediate direction, σ_2, is perpendicular to the plane of the page and so is not shown.

The fractures that form at a moderate angle to the walls of the fault zone (labelled R in Figure 4.5) display the same sense of shear as the main fault. The conjugate (R′) shears are much less commonly developed, but when present form at a high angle to the zone walls with the opposite sense of shear. The fractures in Figure 4.4 are at an angle of around 30° to the fault zone and thus are R-shears. They show a sinistral sense of shear and so we should expect the main fault to have a sinistral shear sense as well.

Figure 4.6 For use with Question 4.2. Looking down on a fault zone, Ramghat valley, Pakistan Himalayas. The edges of the fault zone are marked and the minor fractures are arrowed.

Question 4.2 What is the sense of movement across the fault zone shown in Figure 4.6?

4.1.2 Evidence from fault system geometry

Many of the observations we have already made concerning thrust geometries have implications for their kinematic interpretation.

Question 4.3 Refer back to Section 2.2 and list the properties of thrust systems that have a kinematic significance.

The evidence we have assembled so far principally stems from the geometry of imbricate slices and the realization that thrusts ramp up to a higher structural level in the direction of transport of their hanging-wall. This is such a widely observed phenomenon that it has often been stated as a *rule* of thrust behaviour.

Question 4.4 What is the sense of movement implied by the imbricate slices shown in Figure 2.10?

However, as with all the best rules in nature this one is made to be broken and most sections drawn through thrust systems show the existence of thrusts that branch and ramp in the opposite direction. These are usually referred to as **backthrusts** and one way in which they can develop is shown in Figure 4.7.

Figure 4.7 Development of a backthrust. (a) A fold develops around the tip of a propagating thrust. (b) Continued propagation and displacement results in the formation of both a frontal ramp and a backthrust. The wedge of rock between the two thrusts is referred to as a pop-up.

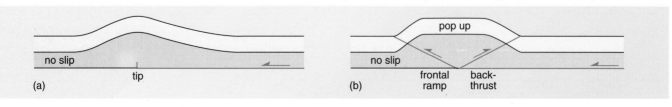

These comments have referred to the movement *sense* that can be inferred from the thrust geometry. Strictly speaking, we have not drawn conclusions regarding the movement *direction* for one very good reason; as we observed in Section 2.2, cross-sections through thrust belts tend to be drawn parallel to the inferred movement direction. So we must ask the question, how has the movement direction been determined in the first place? Small-scale evidence such as slickensides can be used but is associated with the limitations we have already discussed. However, the plan view of the thrusts themselves provides useful information.

We can employ a simple empirical relationship known as the **bow-and-arrow rule**. This is illustrated in Figure 4.8 and states that the best estimate of the movement direction is given by a line at right angles to the chord joining the ends of the curving fault trace. The movement sense is from the chord towards the fault, in other words the direction that an arrow would travel if the curving fault was indeed a bow.

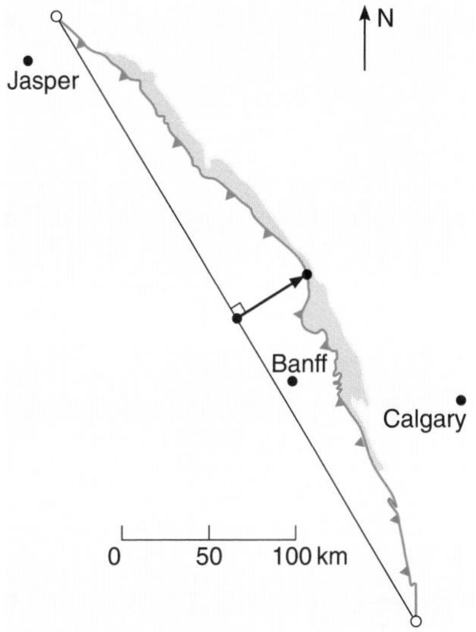

Using both small- and large-scale structural features, it is often possible to establish the directions of movement in the Outer Zones of orogenic belts. Without obvious marker horizons to connect hanging-walls with footwalls, however, there often remains an uncertainty regarding the exact distances that the displaced blocks of rock have travelled. This is the case in the Western Alps where, from the evidence of the thrust geometries, we can be sure that the rocks of the Sub-Alpine Chains have moved to their present position from the east. However, there is still uncertainty as to just how far they moved. They may originally have overlain the basement of the External Crystalline Massifs and the Inner Zone, or, in part, they may have come from areas even further to the east.

Figure 4.8   Sketch map of the McConnell thrust, Canadian Rockies, illustrating the application of the bow-and-arrow rule.

4.2   Shear zone kinematics

Interpretation of the displacement patterns represented by the ductile structures of the Inner Zones can be difficult because of the scale of the structures. Individual structures provide information on the local picture, but the large numbers of shear zones and folds involved means that it is not an easy task to integrate the local information and reveal the 'big picture'. The principles involved, however, are not difficult to develop.

Shear zone kinematics are quite straightforward; we have already seen how a mineral stretching lineation marks the shear direction. If we can add shear sense information to that, we would have a more complete picture, and there are several lines of evidence that can give us this information. Collectively, they are known as **shear criteria**. The combination of a stretching lineation and one or more shear criteria enables us to determine that the block of rock on one side of a shear zone has moved in a specific direction with respect to the other. This is usually expressed in terms of the movement being dextral (opposite block moved to the right) or sinistral (opposite block moved to the left). However, if the shear zone is flat lying, it is often useful to speak of the compass direction in which the block forming the top of the shear zone has moved. For example, shear zones involved in the emplacement of the Inner Zone nappes in the Western Alps could be described as having a top-to-the-west sense of movement.

4.2.1 Shear criteria

Porphyroclast microstructures

In addition to grain size reduction and ribbon grains (Section 3.3.3), there is a further group of microstructures that are characteristic of rocks that have experienced ductile shear. Look at the mylonitic texture in Figure 4.9. A number of larger grains have the foliation wrapping around them. In some ways, this texture is reminiscent of that produced by the growth of porphyroblasts during the deformation of regionally metamorphosed rocks. However, these grains are not growth structures but are the less-deformed remnants of earlier grains and are termed **porphyroclasts**. Their shape is often asymmetric and that asymmetry relates to the sense of shear.

Figure 4.9 Photomicrograph of highly sheared mylonites derived from Lewisian gneiss, Arnaboll Thrust, Moine Thrust Belt, NW Scotland. The larger grains are asymmetric feldspar porphyroclasts. Viewed under crossed polars; width of image = 3 mm.

There are two principal mechanisms by which textures with this pattern can be formed. The first, illustrated in Figure 4.10, is particularly important in mylonites. The porphyroclast is broken down to sub-grains by deformation around its edges and the progressive shear streaks out these sub-grains to form the asymmetric tails of the grain. The sense of shear follows directly from the asymmetry of these tails because, on each side of the grain, the tail extends in the direction of the half-arrow that shows the shear sense. In the case of Figure 4.10, it is dextral.

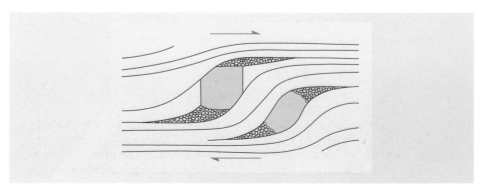

Figure 4.10 Generation of asymmetric porphyroclast tails due to streaking out of sub-grains derived from the host grain.

The second mechanism results from rotation of the porphyroclast in the flow, generating higher stress and lower stress areas at the opposing corners as shown in Figure 4.11. The lower stress zones are favoured sites for deposition of minerals that are carried in solution in the pore fluid. The minerals often grow in a fibrous pattern and produce roughly triangular-shaped areas known as **pressure shadows**. The pressure shadows are asymmetric with respect to the shape of the grain but in this case the 'tails' spread out from the porphyroclast with the opposite sense of asymmetry when compared to the shear that causes the rotation.

S–C mylonites

Mylonites frequently show more than one planar fabric, for example in Figure 4.12.

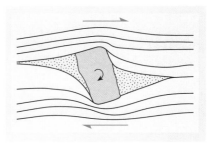

Figure 4.11 Generation of asymmetric porphyroclast tails due to the rotation of the grain. The stippled areas represent fibrous mineral growth in low stress areas located on opposite corners of the grain.

(a)

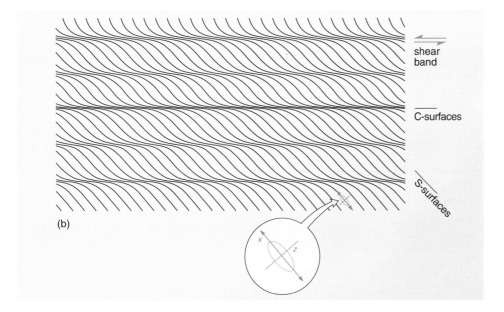

(b)

Figure 4.12 (a) Photograph of S–C mylonite from Tato Road, Nanga Parbat (width of image = 20 cm). The mylonitic foliation ('S'-surfaces) curves in and out of bands of higher intensity shearing ('C'-surfaces). (b) Sketch of ideal S–C geometry. The curvature of the 'S'-surfaces reveals that the 'C'-surfaces, and by inference the entire zone, have a sinistral sense of shear.

There is nothing unusual in rocks showing more than one planar fabric. It is generally diagnostic of rocks having undergone more than one episode of deformation and we will make considerable use of this in the next Section. What is remarkable about mylonites, though, is that the two fabrics appear to develop in response to a single progressive shearing event. The feature was first described by French geologists and the name, S–C, derives from following the standard convention of using 'S' to designate the foliation that is defined by flattened grains, and 'C' to designate bands of higher intensity shearing (after the French for shearing, *cisaillement*). The **S–C fabric** reveals the heterogeneity of deformation intensity within the mylonite. The S-surface fabric, which exists in the lower deformation intensity areas, is systematically curved as it passes into and out of the higher strain, more intensively sheared, C-surfaces. The C-surfaces are usually parallel to the edges of the mylonite zone and the oblique relationship and curving nature of the S-surfaces reveals the sense of shear of the entire zone as demonstrated in Figure 4.12b.

The S–C structure, then, matches the pattern of curving foliation that we have already noted, on the scale of the entire shear zone, in Section 3.3.1. The sense of this curvature also reveals whether the movement on the shear zone is dextral or sinistral and so we can add this larger-scale feature, the systematic curving of a foliation trace across a shear zone, to our list of shear sense indicators.

> **Question 4.5** Interpret the foliation curvature to determine the sense of shear of the shear zone in Figure 3.16.

4.2.2 Fold vergence in shear zones

In Section 3.3.4, we showed how folds develop as a consequence of movement in a shear zone. It was useful, in that context, to describe the movements in terms of a flow direction and we used the analogy of trails of bubbles in a river. However, there is a very significant difference between the flow in a river and that in a shear zone. In a river, the flowing water is quite separate from the riverbanks, but in a shear zone, the flowing rocks and those of the 'banks' are connected. If this were not the case, we would see a fault between the shear zone and its surrounding rock. The consequence of this 'coupling' is that the block of rock on one side of the shear zone moves, in the direction of the flow, with respect to the other.

A look back at Figures 3.26 and 3.27 shows that folds produced in these conditions are strongly asymmetric.

● How can we distinguish asymmetric from symmetric folds?

● The most useful test for fold asymmetry is to identify a fold pair, that is an antiform and its adjacent synform, and to assess whether there is an alternation of longer and shorter limbs. If the limbs are not of equal length then the folds must be asymmetric.

The direction of flow in the shear zone determines the sense of this asymmetry. If we know the displacement pattern of the shear zone, the asymmetry of the folds can be predicted. More often, though, it is useful to take the evidence of the folds and infer the geometry of the shear zone. In order to be able to do this, we need an unambiguous means of describing the asymmetry of folds and we use the concept of **fold vergence** to do this.

Box 4.1 Vergence of folds

The steps to determining vergence are:

1 Locate a cross-section through an asymmetric fold pair that is approximately perpendicular to the fold axes (Figure 4.13a).

2 Choose a long limb of the fold pair and decide which direction it needs to be rotated in order to curve it around the hinge of the fold and into parallelism with a short limb (Figure 4.13b). Draw, or imagine, the pair of curving half-arrows that represent this rotation.

3 Take the *upper* of these arrows and the vergence direction is the horizontal direction towards which it points (Figure 4.13b).

By 'upper arrow', we mean just that, whether we are dealing with a field exposure or a photograph. It refers to the present-day vertical and is not dependent on whether the folded beds themselves are the right way up or upside down, nor is it dependent on the orientation of the axial planes of the fold pair.

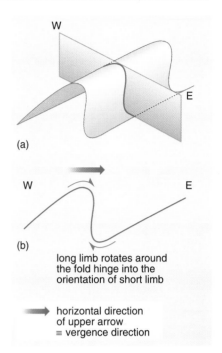

long limb rotates around the fold hinge into the orientation of short limb

horizontal direction of upper arrow ≡ vergence direction

Figure 4.13 (a) Asymmetric fold pair with a plane of section, oriented east–west. (b) Horizontal direction of upper arrow gives the vergence direction.

Fold vergence is a horizontal direction and so is quoted either as a compass bearing (e.g. 045°) or as a point of the compass (NE). We need to examine a cross-section through the fold pair that is as near as possible perpendicular to the fold axis (Figure 4.13a). On such a section, the vergence will be towards one end of the section or the other and so, in the case of Figure 4.13, the vergence could only be either east or west, and the green arrow shows that it is to the east.

Question 4.6 Determine the vergence direction for the folds in Figure 3.26.

So, to return to our example of the Alpine Inner Zone nappes, as they have been emplaced westwards, from the area of the suture, towards the foreland, we would expect the major shear zone-related folds to show a westwards sense of vergence.

4.2.3 Vergence of folds outside of shear zones

A critical phrase in that last sentence is 'shear zone-related folds'. It is important to remember that folding occurs outside of shear zones and many of these folds are found as asymmetric fold pairs, illustrated by the folds in Figure 3.32. It is important to assess whether vergence has any significance when applied to folds in general.

● Determine the vergence directions for the folds in Figure 4.14a and b (overleaf).

● The vergence directions are clearly opposite, south-east in the case of Figure 4.14a and north-west in Figure 4.14b.

We can see from Figure 4.14c that the opposite vergence directions from the two sets of folds do not relate to movements on two different shear zones but that they show a simple relationship to a larger fold. They are minor folds on the limbs of this larger structure. There is, though, a consistent pattern to the vergence in that the opposing vergence directions always point towards the axial planes of the larger antiforms and away from the axial planes of the larger synforms. Furthermore, symmetrical fold pairs can only be found in the hinge

Figure 4.14 (a) and (b) Asymmetric fold pairs. (c) Larger fold showing relationship between the fold pairs in (a) and (b). Folds in Dalradian metasediments, Kilmory Bay, Scotland.

areas of the larger folds. These relationships are summarized in Figure 4.15. It is important to realize that folds showing this behaviour formed during the same deformation episode. They do not relate to multiple deformations.

This property of fold vergence can be very useful in interpreting the structure of an area, particularly where well-exposed cliff faces are not present. Large-scale folding is certainly a spectacular feature (Figures 3.2a, 3.3) but such exposures are rare. Usually, geologists have to infer the large-scale structures from observing minor folds in small outcrops. Careful mapping of changes in fold vergence can locate the axes of the larger folds and identify them as antiforms or synforms.

> **Question 4.7** Use the vergence information on the sketch map (Figure 4.16) to locate the axial traces of the larger folds in the area.

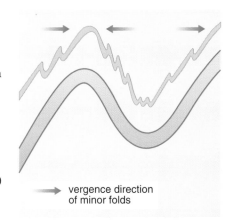

vergence direction
of minor folds

Figure 4.15 The relationship between asymmetric minor folds (orange layer) and major folds (green layer).

Toward antiforms ◊
Away synforms ✗

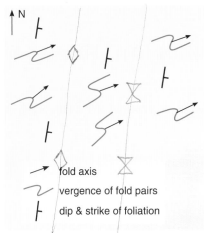

→ fold axis

∿ vergence of fold pairs

⊦ dip & strike of foliation

Figure 4.16 Sketch map locating minor folds. Arrows show orientation of fold axes; *not* direction of vergence. The minor folds are sketched at each location to enable vergence to be determined.

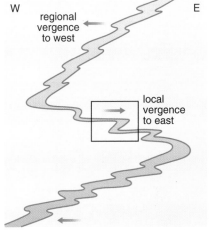

Figure 4.17 Ambiguous relationship between local and regional vergence directions.

This use of the vergence concept was, in fact, the first to be recognized. The use of vergence as a kinematic indicator is a more recent application. However, the two ideas are not entirely compatible and Figure 4.17 illustrates why. The vergence of the larger fold pair suggests a movement direction towards the west, as does the vergence of the minor folds on the top and bottom limbs. The minor folds on the middle limb, though, give the opposite sense of vergence. If these were the only folds visible, we would draw the wrong conclusions regarding the overall movement direction.

Clearly, we need to be cautious when interpreting *local* vergence as an indicator of the *regional* movement direction. Fortunately, as we have seen, there are other indicators of movement sense and so it is not advisable to rely on fold vergence alone. It is important to look at all available lines of evidence and critically re-examine any that give inconsistent results. The best test always has to be one of consistency between the different strands of evidence.

4.2.4 The relationship between foliation and folded bedding

A common observation in folded rocks is that foliation forms roughly parallel to the axial plane of the fold. However, how do the relative orientations of foliation and folded layering vary around an asymmetrical fold? Figure 4.18 depicts a fold pair where the centre limb has been rotated through the vertical and is now upside down, a common occurrence in asymmetric fold pairs.

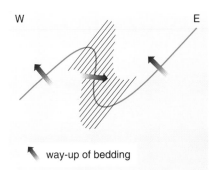

↖ way-up of bedding

Figure 4.18 Fold with way-up arrows showing the middle limb is overturned. The foliation is parallel to the axial plane.

At the fold hinge, the foliation is perpendicular to the bedding, but everywhere else around the fold, the two are at a different angle. This, in itself, can be of vital importance when trying to piece together structures in an area of poor exposure, as we can use it to locate the position of fold hinges. However, there is more information to be gleaned.

Examine the antiformal closure carefully. The overturned nature of the lower limb means that the bedding dips in the same direction (west) on both limbs of the fold. On the upper limb, the dip of the bedding is *less* steep than that of the foliation, whilst on the lower limb it is *more* steep.

○ What is the relationship between bedding and foliation on the limbs of the synformal closure of Figure 4.18?

◑ It is the opposite to the relationship around the antiformal closure. On the upper limb the bedding is *more* steep than foliation, and on the lower limb it is *less* steep.

The critical point is that on a right-way-up limb, foliation is always steeper than bedding and on an inverted limb it is always less steep. However, there may not be any way-up evidence with which to identify the overturned limb. Indeed, with folds of a tectonic fabric, the concept of way-up is irrelevant. But there is still an inverted limb, that is, one that during the evolution of the fold, rotated through the vertical and the relationship to the foliation on the two limbs will still be as described above.

We can make use of this relationship to obtain a **cleavage vergence** direction.

Box 4.2 Cleavage vergence

The cleavage vergence direction is determined by following steps that are very similar to those used for dealing with fold pairs:

1 Locate a cross-section that is approximately perpendicular to the foliation/layering intersection lineation.

2 Choose a fold limb on which the foliation is dipping more steeply than the layering (Figure 4.19a). Decide in which direction the foliation needs to be rotated to bring it into parallelism with the layering. The rotation must be through the acute angle between the two planes (Figure 4.19b). Draw, or imagine, the pair of curving half-arrows that represent this rotation.

3 Take the upper of these arrows and the vergence direction is the horizontal direction towards which it points (Figure 4.19b).

The concept is always referred to as cleavage vergence even though it can be applied to schistosity, providing it formed parallel to the axial planes of folds.

Figure 4.19 (a) Fold limb with cleavage dipping in the same direction as layering but at a steeper angle. (b) Half-arrows illustrating the direction of rotation of the cleavage to bring it into parallelism with the layering. The upper arrow represents the vergence direction.

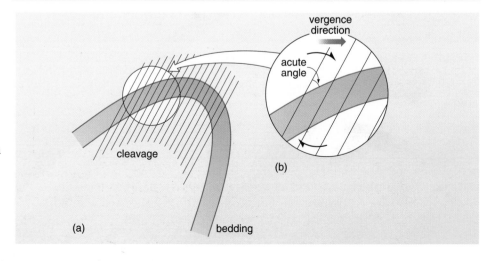

Question 4.8 Figure 4.20 shows outcrops in a cliff face of the same folded
layer. Determine the cleavage vergence direction. Use limb dips to
determine the closing directions of the folds and sketch them onto the
Figure.

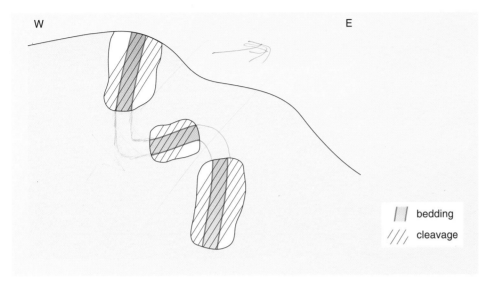

Figure 4.20 Sketch of three outcrops
of the same folded layer. Layering and
cleavage are shown. Middle outcrop
has cleavage steeper than bedding.

Having completed the pattern of the folds, we can now assess the fold vergence
as the middle limb is clearly shorter than the other two.

● What is the direction of vergence determined from the folds?

● You should have come to the surprising result that the folds verge to the
west, the opposite direction to that determined from the cleavage.

At first sight, this would seem to be very unsatisfactory. We have two potential
movement indicators that give opposing results. Figure 4.21 shows a series of
major and minor asymmetric folds. The boxed area in the middle of the diagram
corresponds to the situation in Figure 4.20. The way-up arrows show that the
short limb (A) of this minor fold pair is actually the right way up. It is the entire
short limb of the larger fold, from point B to point C, that is upside down. When
we assess fold vergence, we do so on the assumption that it is the short limb that
has been rotated through the vertical and become inverted. In the case of minor
fold limb (A), this has had the effect of restoring it to its original way up. We can
now resolve the apparent conflict between local and regional vergence that we
noted earlier. It is the cleavage vergence that gives a consistent movement
direction and fold vergence can always be used to locate the larger-scale fold
closures. Used together, there is no ambiguity.

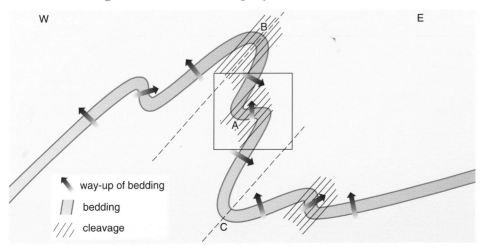

Figure 4.21 Major and minor
asymmetrical folds with way-up
direction shown for each limb. The
boxed area corresponds to Figure 4.20.

Activity 4.1

Now attempt the video-based Activity 4.1, looking at how structures in the Caledonian Orogenic Belt of Scotland can be used to interpret the kinematics of the orogen. You should take about one hour to do this Activity.

Cleavage vergence and fold vergence will always give compatible data providing the foliation and the folds were generated by the same deformation event. In complexly deformed areas, this will not always be the case. In the next Section, we will round off the structural aspects of mountain building by looking at some techniques that we can use to unravel the structures in such situations.

4.3   Summary of Section 4

- The geometry of structures provides information on the movement directions of rock units during orogeny.

- In the case of Outer Zone structures, the geometry of thrust faults gives direct evidence for the movements of the hanging-wall blocks. Small-scale evidence from the fabrics of cataclastic rocks can be used to deduce the large-scale movement patterns.

- The bow-and-arrow rule gives an estimate of movement direction.

- In the case of Inner Zone structures, asymmetric porphyroclasts and S–C fabrics enable the movement directions of individual shear zones to be established.

- Both within and outside of shear zones, fold vergence can be used to establish movement directions, but may relate to local, rather than regional, kinematics.

- Both within and outside of shear zones, cleavage vergence can be used to establish movement directions.

Objectives for Section 4

Now that you have completed this Section, you should be able to:

4.1   Understand the meaning of all the terms printed in **bold**.

4.2   Recognize and interpret those aspects of thrust geometry and cataclastic rocks that give kinematic information.

4.3   Identify shear criteria within ductile shear zones and use them to deduce the kinematics of the shear zone.

4.4   Determine fold and cleavage vergence directions.

4.5   Recognize when vergence directions can be used to deduce movement directions and correctly interpret the evidence.

Now try the following questions to test your understanding of Section 4.

Question 4.9 What information is needed to determine the kinematics of (a) a brittle fault zone and (b) a ductile shear zone?

Question 4.10 Describe the concept of fold vergence.

Question 4.11 Explain the circumstances under which fold vergence and cleavage vergence could show opposing directions for the same fold pair.

5 Using structures — chronology

The Inner Zones of many orogenic belts preserve the greatest structural complexity and have been deformed over considerable periods of time. In the case of the Alps, deformation continued for as long as 100 Ma. Furthermore, the same areas may be deformed by more than one orogenic episode. For example, the Alpine events emplaced thrust slices that include rocks which were deformed and metamorphosed during the much earlier Variscan orogeny. In the Himalaya, the orogen is a result of a Tertiary event (Section 1) although many of the high-grade rocks were also deformed and metamorphosed during the Late Proterozoic Pan-African orogeny that affected much of Gondwana. In both examples, and in many other orogens, the later deformation overprints and modifies earlier structures. Thus, rocks in collisional orogens commonly show a polyphase deformation history and it becomes necessary to unravel a sequence of events.

Box 5.1 Tectonic shorthand

When we begin to analyse the tectonic structures found in complexly deformed areas, we soon recognize evidence for a sequence of events. Geologists have developed a shorthand notation for the description of these sequences, based on letters to identify the class of structure and a numerical subscript to indicate its position in the order of events. The structures that are usually labelled in this way are folds (F), planar fabrics (S) and linear fabrics (L). In addition, the events themselves are often labelled using D for a deformation event and M for a metamorphic event. So, the first deformation would be labelled D_1. During D_1, any folds that form would be called F_1. If these F_1 folds showed an axial plane cleavage, this would be termed S_1 and so on.

It is important to realize that all three classes of structure (F, S and L) *can* form during a single deformation event. However, there is no certainty that they *will* form and even if they did, we may not find evidence for them. Nonetheless, a place would be reserved for them in any table relating structures to events. The consequence of this is that when geologists talk of an S_2 fabric they are not necessarily implying that they have found an earlier planar fabric that could be called S_1. What *is* certain is that they have found some structure, but not necessarily a planar fabric, which can be seen to pre-date the S_2 fabric and which therefore establishes the existence of an earlier deformation event. For example, a geologist may have seen the S_2 fabric cutting across an earlier fold which would thus have to be designated F_1.

However, this rule does not apply to metamorphic events. Although deformation and metamorphism commonly occur together, this is not always the case. A metamorphic event may occur independently of deformation and the most useful statements are often of the form, 'M_1 reached its peak between D_1 and D_2'.

The traditional view of structural sequences is that structures form in response to discrete deformation episodes and that careful geometric analysis would enable each structure to be assigned to a specific event in the sequence. It was this view which prompted the 'F_1, F_2' structural nomenclature. However, we have already described features that clearly do not conform to this pattern. The best example is the development of folds in shear zones as described in Section 3.3.4. Structures such as these develop as a result of progressive deformations that continually modify and ultimately can destroy, as well as create, structures. The net result is that when the deformation ceases structures can be preserved in all stages of development. They may have distinctly different geometries and orientations and yet still be the product of the same deformation phase.

We must be prepared to accommodate both the discrete and the progressive views of structural development in any analysis as the geometries which result will co-exist side by side. However, there are methods that will often distinguish between them.

5.1 Multiple events in folded rocks

The folded and sheared metamorphic rocks of the Inner Zone present us with some fascinating problems of structural chronology. The contorted layers and fabrics typical of these rocks appear daunting at first sight but applying a few simple rules will enable us to understand the relationships.

At this stage, you may ask yourself why is it important that we develop techniques for separating deformation events? This Block is concerned with unravelling the events that result in mountain building. The purpose of the structural analysis in these Sections is to understand how the component parts of a collision zone have changed their shape and position during the development of the orogen. Structures provide this information but if we attempt to put together kinematic information from structures of different ages, the resulting picture will be highly confused, and almost certainly wrong.

5.1.1 Fold facing

Question 5.1 What is the distinction that we draw between the terms antiform/synform and anticline/syncline?

Given that these pairs of terms have completely independent definitions, it is feasible that an upwards-closing fold of bedding (an antiform) could have the youngest rocks exposed in its core (a syncline). Figure 5.1 illustrates such a possibility.

In order to identify such situations, we must have a means of determining the relative ages of the folded beds and thus draw arrows such as those shown on Figure 5.1. The way-up directions on Figure 5.1 were determined on the basis of graded beds.

● Name two other lines of evidence that will give information on the way-up of sedimentary units.

● The clearest evidence comes from a detailed knowledge of the stratigraphy of the sequence. When that is not available, sedimentary structures within and on the surfaces of beds will provide the evidence. The categories of sedimentary structure that most commonly provide way-up evidence are illustrated in Figure 5.2.

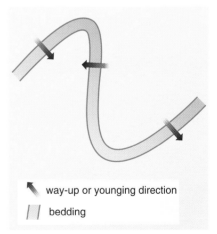

↖ way-up or younging direction

▨ bedding

Figure 5.1   Sketch of antiform and synform pair. The arrows indicate the direction in which the beds become younger and show that the antiform is not an anticline as the rocks in its core are the youngest. The opposite applies to the synform.

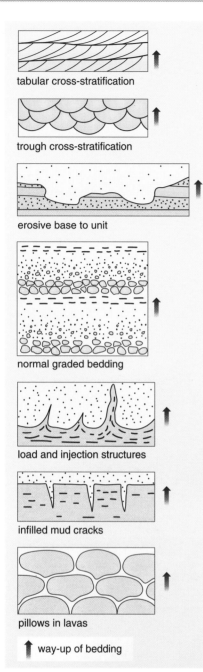

way-up of bedding

Figure 5.2 Summary of the common depositional structures used to determine way-up. All the structures are the right way-up.

In order to avoid rather cumbersome terms such as antiformal syncline etc., we can use the way-up evidence to define a **facing direction** for a fold. This is illustrated in Figure 5.3. Facing is the direction, traced along the axial plane, in which we would encounter younger units.

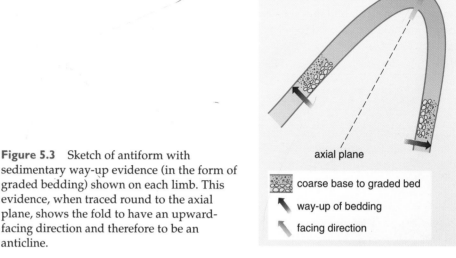

Figure 5.3 Sketch of antiform with sedimentary way-up evidence (in the form of graded bedding) shown on each limb. This evidence, when traced round to the axial plane, shows the fold to have an upward-facing direction and therefore to be an anticline.

If we apply the facing concept to the folds in Figure 5.1, we must conclude that they are downward-facing. As with the closing direction concept, the important aspect of facing is whether it is upwards or downwards, although when folds have flat-lying axial planes we can also talk of facing being towards a particular compass direction.

So, looking at the beds on a single fold limb, we might be able to determine whether they are the right way-up or upside down. By combining the information from the two limbs of a fold, we establish whether the fold itself is upward- or downward-facing.

Question 5.2 Annotate the folds in Figure 5.4 with facing arrows.

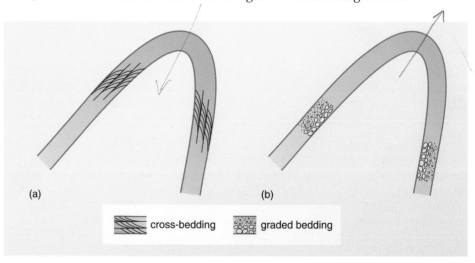

Figure 5.4 Two folds showing sedimentary way-up evidence, for use with Question 5.2.

In order to understand the tectonic significance of fold facing you need to consider how folds can become downward-facing. If you imagine unfolding any downward-facing fold, such as that in Figure 5.1, the beds are still upside down after all curvature of the fold has been removed. This must mean that the beds had previously been subjected to a deformation event, because only deformation can invert strata. The critical conclusion to be drawn from the facing concept is that when folds are downward-facing, more than one generation of folds must be involved.

Figure 5.5 shows two distinct ways in which downward-facing folds can result from two episodes of folding. The original folds (F_1) can be re-oriented to become downward-facing, as in box A, or alternatively new downward-facing folds (F_2) can form on the inverted limb of the earlier structure (box B).

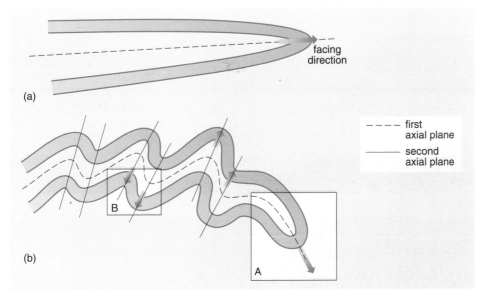

Figure 5.5   (a) Recumbent fold formed during D_1 event. (b) Recumbent fold after re-folding during D_2 to produce re-oriented, downward-facing, F_1 closure (box A) and new, downward-facing, F_2 folds formed on the inverted F_1 limb (box B).

Note, in Figure 5.5b, that the axial plane of the F_1 fold becomes folded by F_2 folds, each of which has a new, unfolded, axial plane.

5.1.2 Multiple tectonic fabrics

We can build on this result because, if folds are modified by later deformation, then the tectonic fabrics that formed in association with them must also be modified. These modifications may take two forms: a pre-existing fabric can itself be folded and/or a second fabric can form, overprinting the first one.

We have already established that planar fabrics, developed during a single period of folding, will be oriented roughly parallel to the axial planes of those folds (Section 3.4). If a planar fabric cuts across both limbs of a fold (Figure 5.6), we can conclude (i) that it did not form at the same time as the fold and (ii) that it developed during a later folding event.

● Why must it be a later, rather than an earlier, event?

● If the fabric was associated with an earlier event, it would have been affected by the later folding and we would expect to see not a set of planes but a set of curving, folded surfaces.

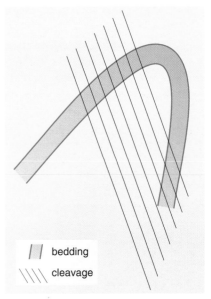

Figure 5.6   Antiform with a later planar fabric cutting across the axial plane of the fold.

Figure 5.7 shows such a curving foliation pattern associated with a typical refolded fold. There is a planar fabric (S_1) parallel to the axial plane of one fold (F_1) and it is folded by a second fold (F_2). Such relationships are unambiguous and form the traditional basis of much structural analysis. The same principles apply to folded lineations as to foliations.

Figure 5.7 Refolded fold of layering, Swiss Alps. The original axial planar foliation has also been folded by the second folding event.

Question 5.3 Identify the first and second generation foliations in Figure 5.8. Label them S_1 and S_2.

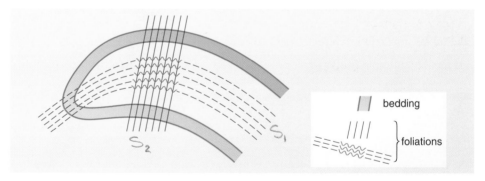

Figure 5.8 Refolded, recumbent fold of bedding with two foliations, for use with Question 5.3.

5.1.3 Fold interference

We have already seen an example of a fold that has itself been folded by a later event (Figure 5.7). In this case, the F_1 axial plane has been folded by the second event. However, this is not the only observation that would indicate that a second set of folds has interfered with an earlier set. The folding of an F_1 axis by later events is equally convincing evidence (Figure 5.9). Note that in this case the outcrop trace of the folded layers forms a closed loop pattern when viewed on a flat surface.

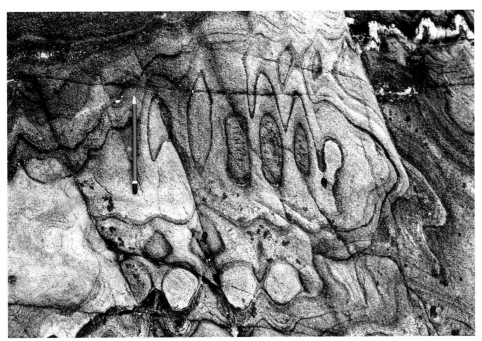

Figure 5.9   Folded Moine metasediments, Loch Monar, Scotland.

⬤   What other feature have we met that results in a closed outcrop pattern?

⬤   This was one of the diagnostic features of sheath folds (Figure 3.9).

Sheath folds, by definition, have strongly curving fold axes and so it is not surprising that they share this geometrical feature with those fold interference patterns that result from the refolding of earlier fold axes. However, the implications for regional tectonics of sheath folds and of multiple deformations are very different. A sheath fold forms as a result of one progressive deformation event whilst an interference pattern requires a second fold set to be superimposed onto an earlier one.

⬤   How could sheath folds be distinguished from a fold interference pattern?

⬤   The most convincing evidence for multiple folding would be the presence of two discrete fabrics associated with the two folding episodes. In the case of a sheath fold, there would only be one fabric.

Activity 5.1

Now do the video-based Activity 5.1, applying these concepts to establishing a chronology of structures in the Caledonian Orogenic Belt of Scotland. You should take about 45 minutes to do this Activity.

5.2   The chronology of thrust systems

In this Section, we have been concerned with folds and fabrics from the Inner Zone, but structural chronology is just as important to understanding the thrust-dominated deformation of the Outer Zone.

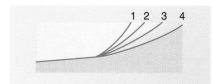

Figure 5.10 A simple imbricate fan.

● Figure 5.10 shows a simple imbricate fan of thrust faults, with the faults numbered 1 to 4. Is it possible to determine the sequence in which the faults developed?

● No. There is nothing inherent in the geometry that distinguishes the sequence in which the faults initiated.

In Figure 5.10, let us assume that the order of thrusting is 1, 2, 3, 4. In this case, the deformation starts at the left-hand end of the section and gradually affects more and more of the rock as successive faults propagate. This makes sense mechanically as, on the scale of the orogenic belt, it would require the deformation to initiate at the line of contact between the converging plates and gradually spread outwards into the foreland. We would expect this pattern to be repeated by structures at smaller scales throughout the orogen. Such a sequence of thrust development is called **piggyback thrusting**, because when a lower thrust propagates and becomes active, any earlier thrust will be present in its hanging-wall and therefore be carried along in piggyback fashion.

Piggyback thrusting may be the norm in many circumstances, but it is instructive to examine the reverse situation, from a mechanical point of view. In this case, imagine thrust 4 is moving first (Figure 5.10). Over time, the fault will propagate, increasing in length, and as it does, so the volume of rock that has to be moved in its hanging-wall must also increase. The greater the volume of rock which must be moved, the greater the shear stress required to cause that movement. Eventually, the required level of stress will exceed the failure strength of the rock. The material of the hanging-wall then fractures, resulting in thrust 3 (Figure 5.10). Now, movement on thrust 3 requires the displacement of a smaller volume of material and so that will become the active fault in the system. We can envisage this process being repeated as each fault, in turn, propagates further into previously undeformed material. This order of thrust development is termed **break-back thrusting**. Figure 5.11 summarizes both sequences of thrust development.

Figure 5.11 (a) Sequence of fault development during piggyback thrusting. (b) Sequence of fault development during break-back thrusting.

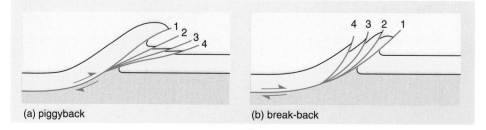

(a) piggyback   (b) break-back

On the largest scale, there seems little doubt that a piggyback sequence of thrust development should operate; it makes no sense for the outer parts of a belt to have been deformed before the inner. However, on the scale of individual duplexes and imbricate fans, both sequences are possible and we should not always assume that piggyback thrusting describes the correct sequence in multiple thrust zones.

Figure 5.12 illustrates a somewhat more complex, but quite typical, sequence. Initially, a piggyback sequence of imbricate faults developed (faults 1–4), and these were then affected by a break-back thrust (fault 5) that developed, piggyback fashion, into a second imbricate fan (faults 5, 6 and 7).

Figure 5.12 Sketch of an Outer Zone thrust belt.

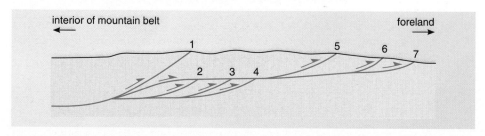

We should expect that thrust belt structures will form from a mixture of a dominant foreland-propagating thrust sequence and the occasional break-back fault. These break-back faults will form as the system adjusts to a changing stress field acting on varied lithologies. The information we need to extract is concerned with the broad pattern of propagation of the thrusting and its associated folding. So, fortunately, it is not necessary to unravel every duplex, so long as the direction in which the deformation was propagating over time can be recognized.

5.3 Discrete and progressive deformation sequences

When these concepts of structural chronology are applied on the scale of an orogenic belt, one of the most important results is that it becomes possible to recognize when structures are the product of discrete deformation events. We already mentioned the case of the External Crystalline Massifs of the Alps, and the Inner Zone rocks of the Scottish Caledonides also provide examples of discrete deformations. Rocks from the Grampian Group provide the basement onto which the Dalradian sediments were deposited and contain structures that pre-date that sedimentation. Those features were subsequently highly modified by structures developed during the Grampian Orogeny.

In both cases, structural analysis allows the geologist to separate discrete events that are suggested by such features as downward-facing folds or multiple tectonic fabrics. We can contrast these features with structures developed during progressive deformation, such as shear zone folds. Any analysis of these folds that attempted to assign them to separate events would

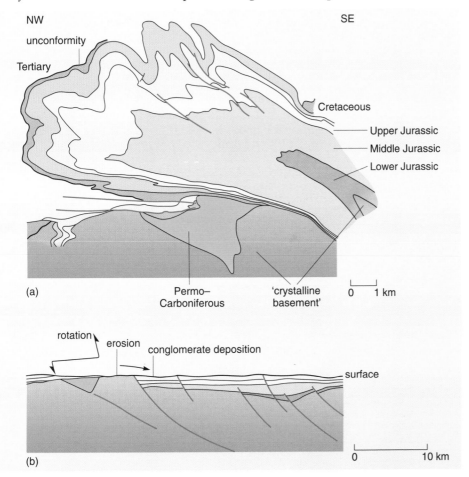

Figure 5.13 A reconstruction of the Morcles nappe. (a) The present distribution of the rocks in the fold profile. (b) The reconstructed stratigraphy of the Mesozoic and Tertiary rocks.

be doomed to failure and almost certainly consign the geologist involved to therapy. It is only by recognizing that they form a sequence related to one progressive deformation event that we can use them to demonstrate the kinematics of that event.

The study of deformation reveals important aspects of the tectonic history of an area. In particular, a kinematic picture, derived from careful observations of an outcrop or even a thin section, can be related to the plate-scale movements responsible for an orogenic belt. However, it would be impossible to make sense of the kinematic picture if the order in which the movements took place — the structural chronology — were not correctly identified.

Although unusual, there are examples where the geometry, kinematics and chronology of the tectonic events that affected an area are all well understood. This allows the geologist to 'see through' the effects of the deformation and restore the stratigraphy to its original state, and the term for such a reconstruction is a **balanced section**. Although it is beyond the scope of the Course to detail the methodology involved, we can conclude this Section with an impressive example. Figure 5.13a shows the Morcles nappe from the Helvetic Alps of Switzerland that was referred to earlier in Section 3 (Figure 3.3). Figure 5.13b shows a cross-section that has been restored to its original state without any gaps or overlaps between fault-bounded blocks — a balanced section.

We have now taken structural analysis far enough to tackle the tectonic history of the spectacular collision zone of the Himalaya. Before we do so, however, we need to consider the thermal processes that operate alongside deformation in more detail.

5.4 Summary of Section 5

- Structures form in response both to discrete deformation phases and to a single progressive deformation.

- The facing direction of a fold defines the relative ages of the folded beds.

- Folds that have downward-facing can only be formed as a result of two or more, discrete deformation events. Downward-facing folds can be either early folds that have had their axial planes re-oriented or they can be new folds generated during the second deformation event.

- The presence of multiple tectonic fabrics in deformed rocks is indicative of two or more discrete deformation events.

- Closed outcrop patterns can also be an indicator but there must be also be evidence of multiple fabrics to distinguish between fold interference and sheath folds.

- On the scale of an orogenic belt, thrust imbrication develops as a piggyback sequence. At smaller scales both piggyback and break-back sequences can develop.

- A full understanding of the geometry, kinematics and chronology of tectonic events can lead to the construction of a balanced section.

Objectives for Section 5

Now that you have completed this Section, you should be able to:

5.1   Understand the meaning of all the terms printed in **bold**.

5.2   Distinguish between the effects of discrete and progressive deformation events.

5.3   Identify and interpret the facing direction of folds.

5.4   Recognize the presence of multiple tectonic fabrics and relate them to the corresponding deformation events.

5.5   Describe the geometries produced by piggyback and break-back sequences of thrust imbrication.

Now try the following questions to test your understanding of Section 5.

Question 5.4 Define the term 'fold facing direction'.

Question 5.5 Draw annotated sketches to illustrate piggyback and break-back sequences of thrust imbrication.

Question 5.6 Folds mapped in a part of the Inner Zone of an orogenic belt show a variety of styles and orientations. What is the critical evidence that would enable you to decide whether they were formed in a shear zone or whether they represent the products of two or more discrete deformation events?

6 Heat flow and metamorphism

During mountain building, the rocks that make up a mountain belt are subject to powerful mechanical forces leading to their deformation. We can learn a great deal from examining the structures of rocks observed on the surface, but the thermal history of these rocks is equally important for understanding how mountains are formed because heat flow and tectonics are closely linked. Geologists have developed a range of heat-flow models that predict how temperature will vary with depth under different tectonic conditions. This allows them to apply the metamorphic information extracted from the rocks themselves in order to understand the tectonic evolution of the belt. This Section is concerned first with simple heat-flow models for the continental geotherm and secondly with interpreting metamorphic assemblages from orogenic belts within the context of such models.

6.1 Thermal history

The rate at which temperature increases with depth in the Earth varies from one area to another. The curve of temperature plotted against depth is called the geotherm (Figure 6.1). The fact that temperature increases with depth requires that the Earth has internal sources of heat. For the continental lithosphere, about 40% of this heat arises from the decay of radioactive isotopes within the upper crust and the remainder is derived from greater depths.

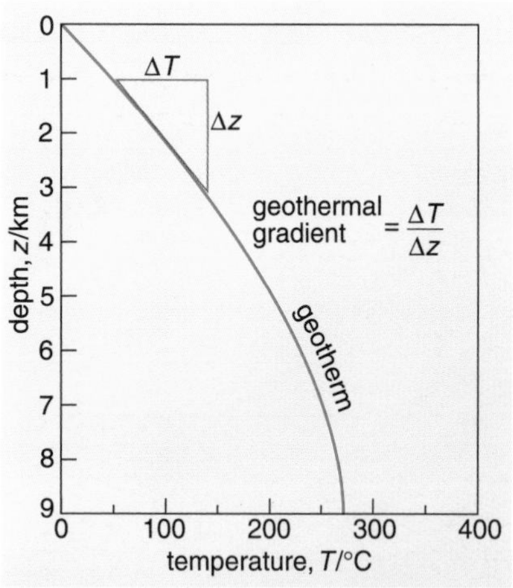

Heat within the Earth transfers by conduction or convection. Within the continental crust, *conduction* is the principal mechanism although convection can also be important where magmas or fluids are migrating through the crust. For the moment, we shall consider only heat conduction.

Figure 6.1   Graph of temperature against depth showing the geothermal gradient expressed as the gradient of a straight line $\Delta T/\Delta z$.

6.1.1 The steady-state geotherm

When the upward **heat flow** towards the surface, q, remains constant with respect to time, the change in temperature with depth is called the **steady-state geotherm**. The geothermal gradient will only change from the steady state if it is perturbed by changing the thickness of the lithosphere, or by intruding magmas or fluids. If we assume that heat flows in a direction perpendicular to the Earth's surface, the relationship between heat flow and the geothermal gradient is given by

$$q = k\frac{\Delta T}{\Delta z} \tag{6.1}$$

where k is the **thermal conductivity** of the rock and the geothermal gradient and $\Delta T/\Delta z$ is measured in °C m^{-1} (equivalent to K m^{-1}). Heat flow, q, is usually measured in W m^{-2} (a watt is a joule per second), so thermal conductivity has units of energy per unit distance per degree per unit time, measured in W m^{-1} K^{-1}.

The heat flow at the Earth's surface in the ideal steady state can be divided into two components:

- heat produced in the mantle;

- heat produced in the crust.

If q_s is the heat flow at the surface and q_m the heat flow at the Moho, then the relationship between q_s and q_m is given by

$$q_s = q_m + A \times d \tag{6.2}$$

where A is **heat production** (measured in W m^{-3}) in the crust and d the thickness of the crust (in m).

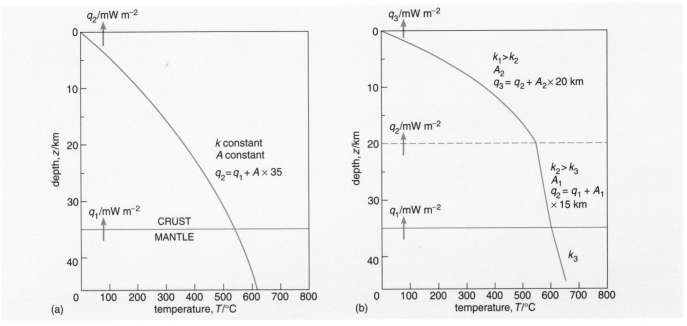

Figure 6.2 (a) Geotherm for crust of uniform thermal conductivity, uniform distribution of heat-producing elements, and constant mantle heat flow. (b) Geotherm for crust with layers of different conductivities and abundances of heat-producing elements.

We know from Equation 6.1 that the geothermal gradient in any part of the crust will be related to the heat flow and thermal conductivity of the rocks in that region, so that if the geotherm is linear — i.e. there is no radioactive heating ($A = 0\,\mathrm{Wm^{-3}}$) and so all heat is derived from the mantle — it is the variation in conductivity k from rock type to rock type that determines the geothermal gradient.

Where the consequences of radioactive decay within the crust are taken into account, the situation becomes more complicated. For a crust of uniform conductivity and uniform heat production, the geotherm defines a curve which is convex upwards (Figure 6.2a). Steady-state crustal geotherms are, therefore, smooth curves in homogeneous rock with sharp changes in gradient only when a rock with a different thermal conductivity is encountered (Figure 6.2b).

Direct measurements of the geotherm are restricted to the upper few kilometres of the crust. Measurements from a borehole in gneissic rocks suggest a linear geotherm for the upper 8 km of crust (Figure 6.3a). However, these measurements give little information about the shape of the geotherm at depth. Figure 6.3b shows three geotherms that give the same value for surface heat flow.

> **Question 6.1** What can you say about the distribution of heat-producing isotopes in the crust and about mantle heat flow from the three geotherms in Figure 6.3b?

Geotherms (1) and (2) represent end-members of a continuous series of geotherms that result from the distribution of the heat-producing elements within the crust and therefore on the lithologies and structure of the crust.

The most important radioactive isotopes for heat production in the continental crust are ^{40}K, ^{232}Th and ^{238}U. Because continental crust has greater abundances of these heat-producing isotopes than the mantle, geotherms steepen sharply from sub-continental mantle to upper continental crust. Models of crustal heat production depend on (i) a knowledge of crustal structure, (ii) direct measurements of heat-producing elements in exposed rocks and (iii) assumptions about their distribution at depth. Modelling heat flow through oceanic crust is a simple matter as it is made up of relatively homogeneous

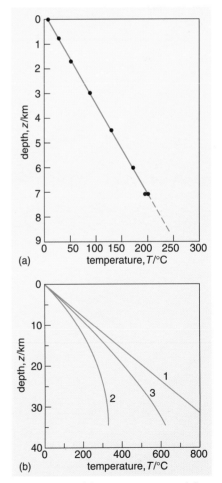

Figure 6.3 (a) Measurements of the geotherm from gneissic rocks, Germany. (b) Three geotherms producing the same surface heat flow and with the same near-surface geothermal gradient.

basaltic material with a thin veneer of sediment. For continents, the crust is far more complex but is most simply considered as a stack of layers, each layer having uniform thickness, heat production and conductivity. For example a highly simplified crust might consist of an upper cover of sediments and/or volcanics that is underlain by a basement of metamorphic rocks which is depleted in the elements K, Th and U as the result of metamorphism and melting. In general, modelling of any steady-state geotherm requires a knowledge of the following parameters:

* the thickness of the major lithological units;

* variation of thermal conductivity and heat-producing isotopes between rock types;

* heat flow from the mantle.

6.1.2 Transient geotherms

So far, we have considered a rather idealized case of equilibrium between heat production and heat flow in rock units of fixed thickness and position in the Earth's crust. To get closer to reality, we now begin to evaluate some of the changes that take place during mountain building and metamorphism.

Changing the geothermal gradient by conduction is a slow business both because of the enormous masses of rock involved and because most rocks are poor conductors. There is a time lag between a disturbance of the steady state, such as that which would result from increasing the thickness of the crust, and the establishment of a steady-state geotherm in the newly thickened crust. The slow change from a disturbed geotherm to the steady-state situation is called **thermal relaxation**. Any geotherm that exists during this period of thermal relaxation is called a **transient geotherm**. For a transient geotherm in normal crust to relax to a new steady-state geotherm can take tens of millions of years. And because some tectonic events such as erosion and major thrusting proceed in less time than is required for thermal relaxation, the geotherm may never get a chance to reach a steady state until these geological changes have ceased. As a result, during orogeny the thermal state of the crust will be continually changing in response to changes in structure imposed by folding and faulting.

Many of the processes in orogenesis involve movement of hot (or cold) materials by *mechanical* means; e.g. the accumulation of thick sedimentary sequences, the formation of nappes, erosion and isostatic uplift, intrusion of magmas and the migration of hydrothermal fluids. In orogenic belts, the evolution of the geotherm in a particular area is therefore the consequence of the interplay between mechanical movement of heat and thermal relaxation by conduction. We shall now consider three examples of transient geotherms resulting from geological processes.

Burial metamorphism

Figure 6.4 is a *P–T* diagram illustrating the thermal effects of burial. Sediments accumulate in basins over tens of millions of years during which the underlying material subsides. The same is true for the accumulation of volcanic rocks in large volcanic provinces, such as those associated with plumes. This progressive burial represents a downward transport of initially cold rock as even lavas will chill to surface temperatures shortly after their eruption.

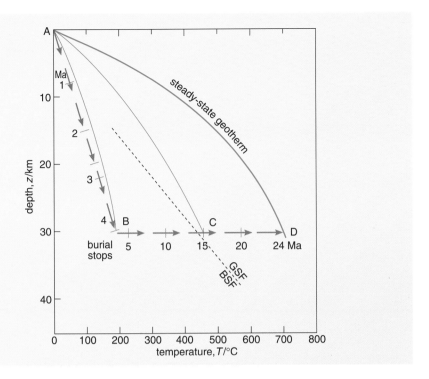

Figure 6.4 Path (arrowed) followed by sediment in *P–T* space during 4 Ma of rapid burial, followed by 20 Ma of thermal relaxation. Transient geotherms are indicated by thin red lines. Subsequent uplift is ignored. Dashed line indicates boundary between blueschist facies (BSF) and greenschist facies (GSF).

There are two factors which will govern the rate at which the buried rocks will heat up: their own heat production and the heat flowing through the materials on which they were deposited. If the rate of burial is the same or slower than the rate of thermal relaxation, then the steady-state geotherm will be maintained. If burial is more rapid, then the geotherm will be cooled because relatively cold rocks have been moved to greater depths (by burial) faster than heat from both the mantle and their own heat production can warm them up. The result is a transient geotherm. If sedimentation ceases, the rocks gradually warm up and return to a steady-state geotherm. But how quickly must burial take place for a low transient geothermal gradient to develop?

> **Question 6.2** From Figure 6.4, calculate the rate of burial required (in mm yr^{-1}) for sediments to follow the *P–T* path A–B.

When burial stops, the sedimentary pile will heat up towards the steady-state geotherm. In Figure 6.4, a sediment at the surface (A) is buried rapidly to a depth of 30 km such that its temperature is only 200 °C. At this time, the transient geotherm will be the slightly curved red line A–B. During the next 20 Ma, this relaxes to a steady-state geotherm (A–D). The arrowed path followed by the sediment in Figure 6.4 (A–B–D) is the **pressure–temperature–time path**.

● What is represented by the red line A–C on Figure 6.4?

● A–C is a transient geotherm 15 Ma after burial started.

In fact, the fate of the sedimentary pile of Figure 6.4 is oversimplified. If burial results in a thickened crust, uplift will follow due to isostasy. Uplift followed by erosion will cause the rocks to be brought upwards towards the surface. Such a process can ultimately lead to the exposure of the rocks at the surface. In other words, they are exhumed.

● What are the thermal consequences of exhumation?

● Rocks at depth are hotter than those at shallower levels, and so the effect of exhumation is to move hotter rocks nearer to the surface.

If the rate of exhumation is faster than the rate at which the rocks cool by conduction, and it usually is, both the surface heat flow and the geothermal gradient increase. In Figure 6.5, rock A initially lies on a steady-state geotherm at a depth of 30 km, and is subsequently exhumed to the surface (C) in 20 Ma. It follows the arrowed path A–B–C, and at each point on the path it will lie on the prevailing transient geotherm. After 10 Ma of exhumation the transient geotherm is given by the thin red line B–C.

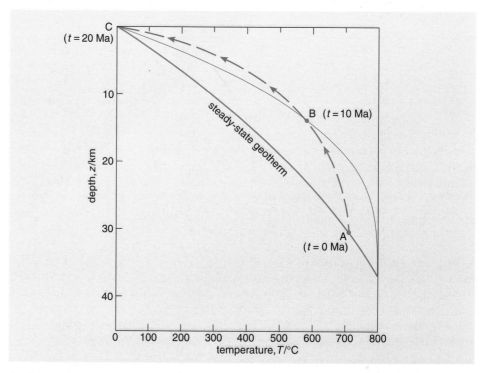

Figure 6.5 Exhumation of rock that lies initially on a steady-state geotherm at a depth of 30 km (A). This red line indicates transient geotherm 10 Ma after exhumation begins.

An important implication of this analysis is that, if the initial conditions at the deepest part of the pressure–temperature–time path (e.g. at point B in Figure 6.4) are to be preserved by metamorphic minerals brought up to the surface, they have to be exhumed from these depths rapidly before they heat up and change mineralogy. So, the metamorphic mineral assemblage preserved in a rock depends partly on its rate of exhumation relative to the mineral reaction rate. This has important consequences to which we shall return.

Igneous intrusions

Exhumation of warm rock is one form of mechanical transfer of heat, but heat transfer by the upward movement of magmas is likely to be much more rapid.

Large rising igneous plutons, such as granites, transfer heat through convection which greatly distort the transient geotherm (Figure 6.6). At the time of intrusion, the overlying rocks increase in temperature and those rocks at the contact may even be heated to the temperature of the magma. The sudden change in the geothermal gradient in Figure 6.6 is most marked at the roof of the pluton, and in part reflects the fact that the temperature within the intrusion is kept roughly constant by internal convection. After solidifying, the intrusion will cool by conduction of heat into the surrounding cover rocks. The geotherm eventually reaches steady state corresponding to the distribution of heat-producing elements within both the intrusion and cover rocks.

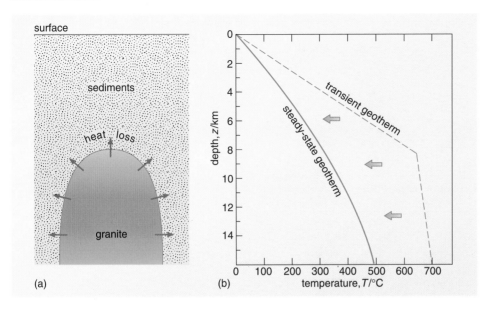

Figure 6.6 (a) Diagram showing a rising granite pluton intruding sediments. (b) Transient geotherm associated with igneous intrusion at the time of its emplacement. Once the magma has crystallized, this will relax towards the steady-state geotherm.

Crustal thickening by thrusting

The most efficient way of thickening the upper crust is by stacking up a series of thrust slices (Figure 2.7) as is commonly observed in the Outer Zones of orogenic belts. This can be modelled by considering a steady-state situation at time t_1 before the orogeny, when isotherms (T_1, T_2, T_3) are horizontal and increase in value with depth along a steady-state geotherm which, for the sake of simplicity, we assume to be linear (Figure 6.7a). At time t_2, a thrust begins to develop, moving some of the rocks of the area A over those of area B (Figure 6.7b); by time t_3, the crust in area B is thickened by the addition of the nappe from area A (Figure 6.7c). Whether this event superimposes a radically different geotherm on area B depends on the rate of thrusting, the thickness of the nappe and its thermal properties.

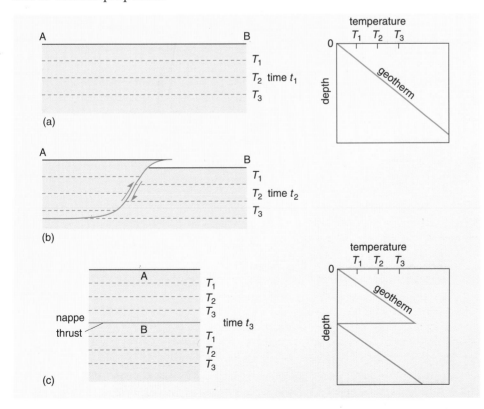

Figure 6.7 (a) Isotherms in undisturbed crust and steady-state geotherm at time t_1 (b) At time t_2 a thrust begins to carry part of the crust at A towards and over area B. (c) Thrusting complete by time t_3 and the 'saw-tooth' transient geotherm reflects a repeated steady-state geotherm in units A and B separated by the thrust.

The temperature–depth graphs for Figure 6.7a and 6.7c show an idealized situation for straight-line geotherms and instantaneous thrusting. What Figure 6.7c amounts to is the stacking of the upper section of a steady-state geotherm on top of another geotherm to give a **saw-tooth geotherm** with a surface temperature 'buried' at considerable depth below much hotter rocks. This is a highly unstable situation, for heat will flow rapidly from the hotter base of the upper sheet into the surface of the lower sheet. The saw-tooth effect is therefore transient. In other words, it must relax with time towards a new steady-state geotherm (Figure 6.8a).

For a while, negative geothermal gradients will be associated with relaxation of the saw-tooth geotherm, as shown in Figure 6.8a (geotherms 1, 2 and 3). But heat will continue to flow upwards as well, so that the initial development will amount to a removal of heat in *two directions* from A. At the same time, B will be warming up from the heat from A and also from its own heat production and deeper heat flow. At some stage, a normal geotherm with positive gradients throughout is achieved (Figure 6.8b, geotherm 4) and the whole pile now begins to heat up towards the steady state (Figure 6.8b, geotherms 4–8).

> **Question 6.3** (a) What can you conclude about the *early* conditions of temperature and pressure on either side of the thrust shown in Figure 6.8a? (b) What is the most important factor for ensuring that this distribution of pressure and temperature can be preserved in metamorphic rocks exhumed at the Earth's surface?

The decrease in temperature with depth in a transient geotherm can result in **inverted metamorphism**: i.e. higher grade metamorphic rocks lying on top of lower grade rocks. It has been recognized in some young orogenic belts and has been taken as evidence for very rapid exhumation rates.

This kind of thermal model is much simpler than any real example is likely to be. Heat flow occurs in three dimensions, not in one, and crustal rocks themselves are very variable in terms of their heat production and thermal productivity. As measurements of surface heat flow are not a useful guide to the

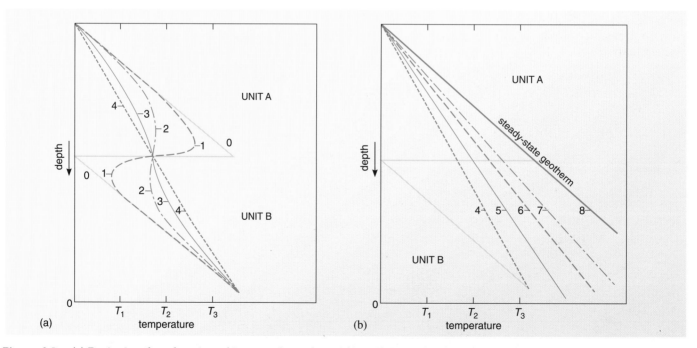

Figure 6.8   (a) Beginning the relaxation of 'saw-tooth geotherm' (time 0). Note the shape of geotherms at times 1, 2 and 3 where there are *decreases* in temperature with depth. By time 4, all the temperatures in unit A are *half* their original values due to loss of heat to surface *and* to unit B. (b) Relaxation of geotherm to the steady state between time 4 and time 8. All the geotherms are 'normal' (i.e. temperatures increase steadily with depth).

shape of the geotherm at depth, the only direct evidence a geologist can gather for the thermal history of an orogenic belt comes from interpreting the minerals exposed at the surface. This is the purpose of metamorphic studies.

6.2 Metamorphic petrology

Metamorphic petrology comprises two distinct but interwoven strands. First, the *texture* of metamorphic minerals can establish when minerals have grown relative to deformation of the rock, and also the sequence in which minerals grew relative to each other. Given appropriate textures, we can therefore build up a framework for deformation and mineral growth through time. Secondly, a metamorphic petrologist can infer the pressure and temperature experienced by the rock at different stages within this time framework. This requires the application of the laws of basic thermodynamics to minerals that formed in equilibrium with each other during metamorphic reactions.

6.2.1 Metamorphic minerals and their textures

Using metamorphic rocks as keys to the thermal history of an orogen depends initially on identifying the minerals present.

Activity 6.1

Now do the video-based Activity 6.1 which will illustrate some of the common metamorphic minerals in thin section. You should take about one hour to do this Activity.

Once you are familiar with the common metamorphic minerals, the next step is to interpret the textural information from metamorphic rocks. Working out the progress of metamorphism in an orogenic belt depends on relating the growth of new minerals to the deformation history based on minor structures. The most useful minerals for this occur as larger crystals, called porphyroblasts, in a finer-grained matrix.

Figure 6.9 Porphyroblasts of kyanite (blue blades) showing random orientation in an outcrop of kyanite–garnet schist.

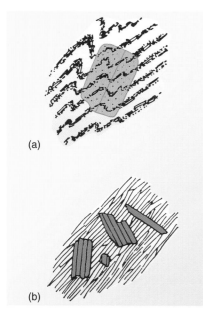

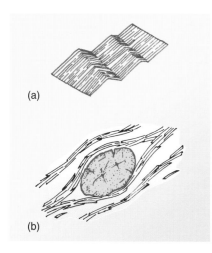

Figure 6.10 Post-kinematic minerals:
(a) andalusite enclosing earlier folds;
(b) mica growing randomly across
earlier cleavage.

Figure 6.12 Pre-kinematic minerals:
(a) folded mica; (b) cracked garnet
wrapped around by foliation.

Deformation in a rock is often identified from the preferred orientation of minerals which form a linear or planar fabric. The relationship of this fabric to porphyroblasts gives an indication of the relative timing of fabric formation (deformation) and porphyroblast growth (metamorphism). In outcrop or hand specimens, you may observe porphyroblasts that grow in random orientation as shown in Figure 6.9. If such porphyroblasts cut across the main schistosity of the rock, they are termed **post-kinematic**. Post-kinematic mineral growth may be recognized in thin section by crystals that grow across an earlier foliation, often retaining a regular, symmetrical outline (Figure 6.10). In more complex cases, post-kinematic overgrowths surround earlier-formed minerals.

Figure 6.11 Porphyroblasts of kyanite showing strong flattening in outcrop of kyanite–garnet schist.

Where porphyroblasts pre-date deformation, their orientation will be parallel to the main schistosity of the rock (Figure 6.11). This texture is termed **pre-kinematic**. Because metamorphism is often a long, complex process accompanied by deformation, early-formed minerals may well be obliterated by both deformation and further metamorphic recrystallization. Pre-kinematic minerals that are preserved will be distinguished in thin section by later strain effects, as shown in Figure 6.12a. Others that are not easily deformed, such as garnet, may be wrapped around by later platy minerals that define a foliation (Figure 6.12b).

The term **syn-kinematic** is applied to minerals that grew during deformation. Platy minerals like mica define the schistosity of mica-rich schists. Elongate, rod-like amphiboles are particularly useful for defining syn-kinematic mineral lineations. More equant, syn-kinematic porphyroblasts, such as garnet, may rotate during shear deformation resulting in curved trails of included minerals as shown in Figure 6.13. Such textures are found in ductile shear zones (Section 3.3).

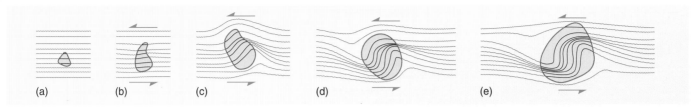

Figure 6.13 Stages in the growth of syn-kinematic garnet porphyroblast during sinistral shear deformation.

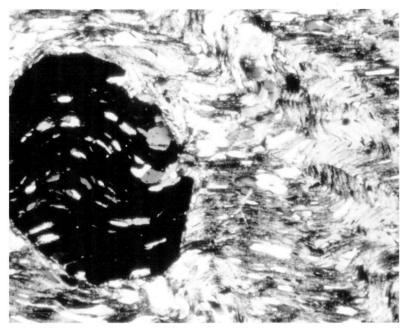

Syn-kinematic

Figure 6.14
Photomicrograph seen
between crossed polars:
width of image = 5.5 mm. For
use with Question 6.4.

Question 6.4 Are the porphyroblasts in Figures 6.14 and 6.15 pre-, syn- or
post-kinematic?

Pre-kinematic

Figure 6.15 Photomicrograph seen between crossed polars: width of image = 5.5 mm.
For use with Question 6.4.

In orogenic belts, metamorphic rocks often record a long and complex history involving more than one period of deformation and metamorphism. For example, inclusion trails within porphyroblasts may retain evidence for an early deformation event. In Figure 6.16, the porphyroblast contains many inclusions that form a rough orientation top-right to bottom-left. This forms a fabric (S_1) that pre-dated the growth of the porphyroblast. In the matrix of the rock, the fine-grained micas are orientated horizontally. This is a younger fabric (S_2) that post-dates the growth of the porphyroblast.

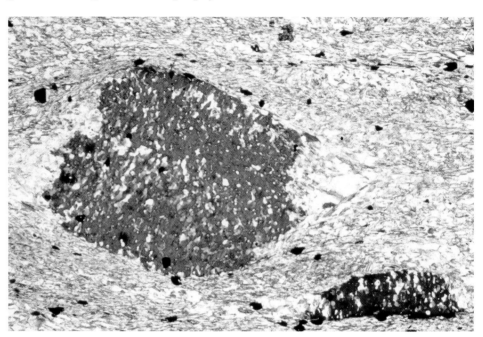

Figure 6.16 Photomicrograph seen in plane-polarized light of a biotite porphyroblast in a muscovite schist: width of image = 5.5 mm.

Micas are particularly useful for recording deformation and in some cases record several events in the same rock even in the absence of porphyroblasts. In Figure 6.17, the micas mostly record a very strong fabric from top-right to bottom-left. However, we know that the single large crystal in the top left-hand corner grew after this early deformation because it is aligned in a different direction to the main fabric.

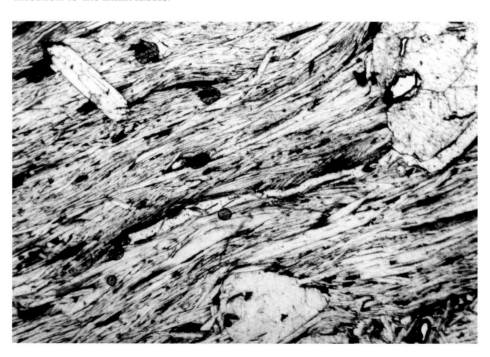

Figure 6.17 Photomicrograph seen in plane-polarized light of a muscovite schist: width of image = 3.5 mm.

Recent developments in isotopic dating techniques allow individual crystals to be dated in a thin section. For the mica schist in Figure 6.17, muscovites forming the main fabric would provide an age for the main deformation event experienced by the rock. The large crystal which grew oblique to this fabric would record a younger age of metamorphism. By combining thin section observations with precise mineral dating, a chronological framework for orogenic events can be built up, as we shall see in Section 7.

6.2.2 Metamorphic reactions

Interpreting metamorphic mineral textures would not be of great value if we could not also assess the pressure and temperature at which the porphyroblast grew. For any given rock composition, pressure and temperature, a specific mineral assemblage is stable. Changing the pressure or temperature will at some stage cause minerals to become unstable and react to form new minerals. Although beyond the scope of this Course, these reactions can be treated from a strictly thermodynamic point of view, as can any chemical reaction. For metamorphic minerals, the reactions result from disequilibria between solid phases and therefore the rate of reactions is often slow. The slow reaction rate of most metamorphic reactions is very useful to petrologists because it commonly allows some part of a rock's history to be preserved during burial, metamorphism and uplift. Otherwise, all rocks would be made up of minerals stable at a pressure of one atmosphere and at surface temperature!

In general, the equilibrium between one mineral and another, or of one assemblage and another, is represented by a line on a P–T graph. For example, to the left of the curved line C–D–E (Figure 6.18), muscovite and quartz are stable. To the right, alkali feldspar, an aluminosilicate (Al_2SiO_5) and H_2O are stable. Only on the line itself are all five phases stable. This equilibrium can be written as:

$$\text{muscovite} + \text{quartz} \rightleftharpoons \text{alkali feldspar} + Al_2SiO_5 + H_2O$$

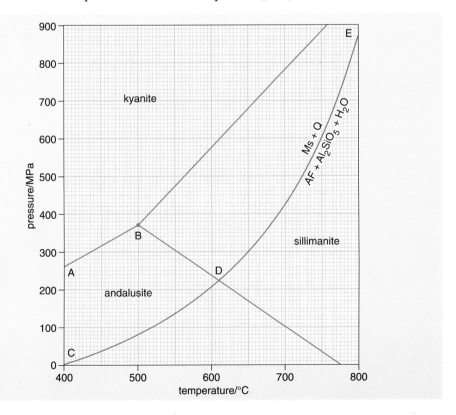

Figure 6.18 P–T diagram for the stability field of the three aluminosilicate minerals with the formula Al_2SiO_5, and of the assemblage muscovite (Ms) and quartz (Q). AF = alkali feldspar.

Since muscovite and quartz are stable at low temperatures, we can represent the up-temperature (or **prograde**) reaction as:

muscovite + quartz → alkali feldspar + Al_2SiO_5 + H_2O

The arrow denotes the direction in which the reaction is proceeding in response to changing temperature and/or pressure.

During a decrease in temperature, a **retrograde** reaction may occur, especially if water is present. A common example is chlorite replacing biotite which you may have seen in thin section. This retrograde reaction is expressed as:

biotite + muscovite + H_2O → chlorite

> **Question 6.5** Figure 6.18 shows stability fields of minerals which are common in pelitic rocks. (a) Over what pressure range is sillimanite stable at 600 °C? (b) What aluminosilicate minerals are in equilibrium at any point on the line A–B? (c) What is different about the minerals in equilibrium between CD and DE? (d) Over what temperature and pressure range is andalusite stable with muscovite and quartz?

An important point to note from Figure 6.18 is that, at higher temperatures, the reaction of muscovite and quartz has a fairly steep slope. This is typical of many mineral reactions in metamorphic rocks, and their steep slopes imply that they are far more sensitive to changes in temperature than they are to changes in pressure. They are termed **geothermometers**, and the reaction involves a large increase in the entropy of the rock as it passes across the equilibrium line with increasing temperature. In other words, the molecular structures of the products are more disordered than those of the reactants. This reflects the presence of H_2O produced by the reaction because the molecular structures of gases are much more disordered than those of solids. As liquids are also more disordered than solids, mineral reactions involving melting also tend to have steep slopes.

To pin down the pressure as well as the temperature at which a metamorphic rock formed, we also require some reactions that are insensitive to temperature but are sensitive to changes in pressure, i.e. reactions that would plot as near-horizontal lines on Figure 6.13. Pressure-sensitive reactions are less common, and they are governed by large volume changes, rather than by large entropy changes. A low-pressure mineral assemblage which reacts to form a higher-pressure assemblage must undergo a net decrease in volume, thus increasing the density of the rock.

> **Question 6.6** From Figure 6.18, which of the three aluminosilicates — andalusite, sillimanite, and kyanite — would you predict has the highest density?

The equilibrium between kyanite and andalusite gives information on the pressure of formation and is therefore a **geobarometer** (although an ideal geobarometer would have a flat equilibrium line, parallel to the temperature axis). If it were possible to find a series of ideal geothermometers and geobarometers, we could then pigeonhole different associations of metamorphic minerals on a P–T graph with great precision. As it is, we have relatively few mineral reactions which are sensitive to pressure, but many geothermometers. This means that the temperature of metamorphism is often better known than the pressure of metamorphism.

Another point about the P–T fields for metamorphic rocks concerns the limitations of the experiments used to define equililbria. These are often undertaken on samples which have days or weeks to equilibrate, not the millions of years available to natural rocks. Many metamorphic reactions are slow, particularly if they involve only solid phases, so there is uncertainty over the position of sluggish, experimentally determined reactions in P–T space. Moreover, the composition of rocks observed in the field are more complex than the assemblages used in experiments, so there will be discrepancies between experimental systems and natural rocks. Despite such difficulties, however, a metamorphic geologist working with a range of rock types with different mineral assemblages can commonly obtain $P–T$ estimates accurate to within a few tens of degrees centigrade and <100 MPa.

Mineral reactions involving the release of fluid phases are also sensitive to the composition of the fluid phase in equilibrium with the solid minerals and it is often difficult to assess the fluid composition that was present during metamorphism. Fluids present during metamorphism are generally combinations of CO_2 and H_2O although small amounts of other gases such as methane, nitrogen or chlorine may be present. Progressive metamorphism of most rocks results in loss of H_2O with increase in temperature, first from the collapse of pore spaces (compaction) and secondly from the progressive dehydration of hydrous minerals (clay minerals, micas or amphiboles). Rocks containing carbonates also undergo decarbonation due to CO_2 release during an increase in temperature. The variation of H_2O and CO_2 contents of fluids during metamorphism is the subject of much debate. It is being resolved by detailed studies of minute fluid inclusions entrapped in minerals during metamorphic growth.

There is one more important variable in relating natural mineral assemblages to $P–T$ diagrams established from experiments. The curves representing mineral equilibria on Figure 6.18 imply that each mineral has a fixed composition, and for minerals such as andalusite, kyanite and sillimanite, that is correct. However, many minerals exhibit *solid solution*. For example, the mineral olivine ranges from Fe-rich to Mg-rich, and in igneous systems the Fe:Mg ratio in olivine varies with the composition of the magma with which it is in equilibrium. In metamorphic rocks, the composition of minerals within a solid solution series varies with the composition of the rock. For example, the equilibrium for cordierite breakdown is given by

$$3(Mg, Fe)_2 Al_4 Si_5 O_{18} \rightleftharpoons 2(Mg, Fe)_3 Al_2 Si_3 O_{12} + 4Al_2 SiO_5 + 5SiO_2$$
$$\text{(cordierite)} \qquad \text{(garnet)} \qquad \text{(aluminosilicate) (quartz)}$$

Both cordierite and garnet are solid solutions, while quartz and Al_2SiO_5 are not. Al_2SiO_5 may be in the form of sillimanite or andalusite depending on the $P–T$ conditions (Figure 6.19).

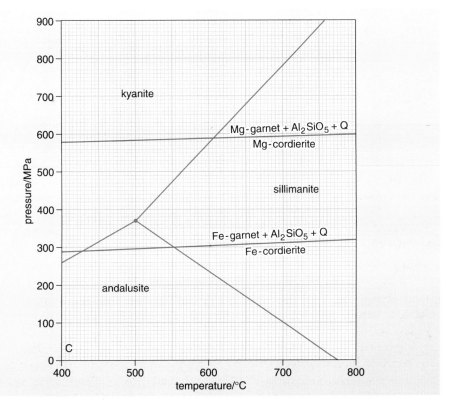

Figure 6.19 $P–T$ diagram for the stability field of cordierite.

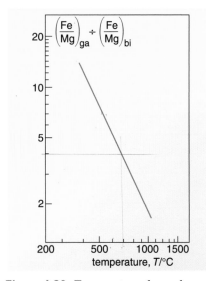

Figure 6.20 Temperature dependence of Fe:Mg (as an atomic ratio) between garnet and biotite in equilibrium. Note that both axes are non-linear scales.

This equilibrium is insensitive to changes in temperature and you can see from Figure 6.19 that it forms a good geobarometer on a *P–T* graph. You will also notice that it is represented by two lines, a low pressure equilibrium for Fe-rich minerals and a high pressure equilibrium for Mg-rich minerals. Natural mineral assemblages will lie somewhere between the two depending on the Fe:Mg ratio of the rock.

> **Question 6.7** A metamorphic rock contains cordierite, garnet, sillimanite and quartz. In the absence of any other information, except that it formed between 600 °C and 800 °C, can you say anything about its pressure of formation?

It is therefore important to know the Fe:Mg ratio of cordierite before we can estimate a more precise pressure from the assemblage cordierite–garnet–sillimanite–quartz.

Most minerals with Fe and Mg in their structure exhibit variable Fe:Mg ratios, and if two different Fe–Mg minerals, such as garnet and cordierite, are in equilibrium, the Fe:Mg ratio of both minerals is related in a way that depends on the temperature. This is illustrated in Figure 6.20, where the Fe:Mg ratio in garnet, divided by the Fe:Mg ratio in biotite that is in equilibrium with it, decreases with increasing temperature. Because the Fe:Mg ratios in garnet and biotite are insensitive to changes in pressure, the distribution of Fe and Mg between these two minerals makes a good geothermometer. Metamorphic temperatures can be estimated directly from the chemical analyses of Fe and Mg in co-existing garnet and biotite assuming that these two minerals were in equilibrium at that temperature.

> **Question 6.8** A pelitic rock contains cordierite, sillimanite, garnet, quartz and biotite. The Fe and Mg contents (in atomic proportions) are 0.8 and 0.2 for the garnet, 0.5 and 0.5 for the biotite, 0.2 and 0.8 for the cordierite. Assuming that these minerals are in equilibrium, what can you deduce about the conditions of temperature and pressure during metamorphism from Figures 6.19 and 6.20? You may also assume a linear relationship between (Fe/Mg)$_{cord}$ and pressure in Figure 6.19.

6.2.3 Metamorphic zones and facies

The study of metamorphic reactions underpins our understanding of the pressures and temperatures at which metamorphic assemblages are formed. But field geologists working in large orogenic belts need to obtain some semi-quantitative information from simply observing the minerals present in a hand specimen. During the 19th century, metamorphic petrologists developed the concept of *metamorphic zones*. Such zones reflect changes in temperature and pressure experienced by rocks of similar bulk composition. Each zone is identified by a characteristic index mineral.

Metamorphic zones were first recognized during field work by George Barrow in the Dalradian metasediments from the Inner Zone of the Caledonides (Section 3.1). In general the Inner Zone of an orogenic belt not only preserves the best examples of ductile deformation, but also of high-grade metamorphism since Inner Zone rocks have been exhumed from deeper crustal levels (Section 3). Barrow mapped out the regular metamorphic sequence, chlorite–biotite–garnet–staurolite–kyanite–sillimanite and these index minerals now give their names to the Barrow zones. Chlorite is found in the rocks of lowest metamorphic grade and sillimanite in rocks of the highest metamorphic grade. Evidence for partial melting is only found in the sillimanite zone.

● Does that mean that each of these index minerals appears in all outcrops successively as the zones are crossed?

● No. The minerals only form when the rock's chemical composition permits.

The key composition used by Barrow is that of aluminous sediments (mudrocks), known as pelites. Such compositions provide mineral assemblages which are particularly sensitive to changes in pressure and temperature. Barrow's initial work was conducted in the Glen Esk section (Figure 6.21). In other parts of the Highlands, slightly different assemblages were found due to different pressures of metamorphism. For example, along the Banff coast the presence of andalusite (rather than kyanite) indicates a lower pressure during metamorphism (Figure 6.21).

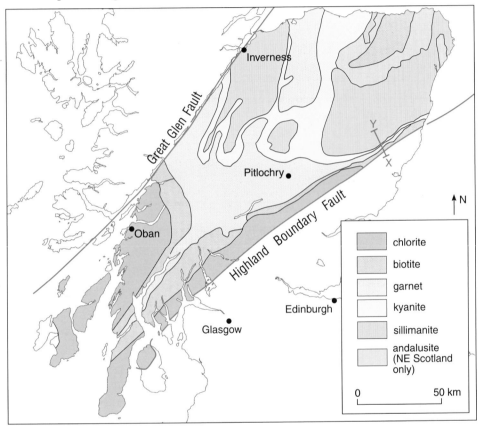

Figure 6.21 Distribution of metamorphic zones throughout Central Scotland. The staurolite zone is a narrow area between the garnet and kyanite zones. The line X–Y is the Glen Esk section. (From J.A. Winchester (1974) 'The regional metamorphic zones in the Scottish Caledonides', *Journal of the Geological Society*, vol. 130, Pt. 6, Nov., Geological Society Publishing House.)

The index minerals mark the *first* appearance of this mineral in rocks of pelitic composition as the zones are crossed in the direction of increasing metamorphic grade. The lower grade index minerals may persist within zones of higher grade assemblages. For example, sillimanite gneisses frequently also contain garnet and biotite.

Activity 6.2

You should now do the microscope-based activity on Dalradian metamorphism. You should take about one hour to do this Activity.

The mapping of metamorphic zones using index minerals is very useful for describing metamorphism from a particular area, particularly where pelitic rocks are common. However, it is difficult to compare the metamorphic grade of different areas on the basis of index minerals because of the possibility of different bulk compositions in the two areas, which may result in different metamorphic minerals even under similar conditions of pressure and temperature. For this reason, a new concept is required.

Metamorphic facies is a term used to embrace *all* the possible metamorphic mineral assemblages produced in rocks of different composition at similar temperatures and pressures.

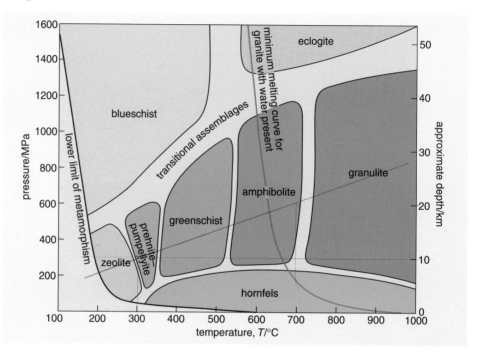

Figure 6.22 The *P–T* fields of the major metamorphic facies.

A *P–T* diagram may be divided into several fields on the basis of the observed mineral assemblages in metamorphic rocks. Such fields are called facies (Figure 6.22). The specific assemblage present in a rock from a given facies will depend upon the composition of the rock. The conditions under which different mineral assemblages are stable are determined experimentally by subjecting a given rock composition to different pressures and temperatures and identifying the stable minerals under equilibrium conditions. The most commonly used rock compositions correspond to pelite, basic igneous rocks and carbonates. This approach gives us a general *P–T* range for each facies.

It is important to emphasize that the metamorphic facies is indicative of a broad range of *P–T* conditions, and the usefulness of mineral facies is that they can often be identified in the field. For example, the appearance of chlorite or epidote in pelitic or basic compositions is generally indicative of the greenschist facies, and their replacement by amphibole suggests somewhat higher grades in the amphibolite facies. The precise *P–T* field of equilibrium for each assemblage requires detailed analysis of mineral compositions, and at this stage of investigation the concept of mineral facies becomes redundant and is replaced by a more precise point or field on a *P–T* diagram.

Question 6.9 For continental crust, the steady-state geotherm is between 30 °C/km and 40 °C/km, depending on the age and thickness of the crust. By sketching linear geotherms with these values on to Figure 6.22, identify which metamorphic facies lie on an average continental geotherm. You may assume the geotherm is at 0 °C at the surface.

The fact that many metamorphic rocks exposed at the Earth's surface are from metamorphic facies not identified in Question 6.9 suggests that rocks can form under conditions that are quite distinct from those defined by steady-state geotherms. In other words, the steady-state geotherm must be disturbed by geological processes.

● What processes could give rise to hornfels-facies conditions?

● Hornfels-facies rocks indicate high temperatures at low pressures. These conditions are only found in the aureoles of igneous plutons, as discussed in Section 6.1.2, so magmatic intrusions are required.

● What processes could give rise to blueschist-facies conditions?

● Blueschist-facies rocks indicate higher pressures at lower temperatures than occur on the continental steady-state geotherm. These conditions can occur during burial in sedimentary basins.

Blueschist-facies conditions also result from the subduction of oceanic crust because cool, near-surface rocks are rapidly taken down to great depths. Importantly, whatever the cause of blueschist-facies conditions, high-P low-T assemblages will only be preserved if exhumation of the rocks is fast enough for the rocks not to heat up during their ascent. If they heat up, then the minerals will recrystallize in different metamorphic facies. For example, blueschist-facies rocks are often partly recrystallized in the greenschist facies during their ascent. On Figure 6.4 the dashed line indicates the boundary between blueschist and greenschist facies. The diagram suggests that unless the rock is exhumed very rapidly, it will recrystallize in the greenschist facies. If such rocks are completely recrystallized then the evidence for their having passed through a high-P low-T field will be lost.

The metamorphic facies of a metamorphic rock can therefore give some general indications of the geological conditions that determined its assemblage. We can now consider how to relate this information more specifically to the evolving geotherm during mountain building and so use metamorphic studies to fingerprint specific tectonic events.

6.3   Metamorphism during mountain building

Any rock exhumed within an orogenic belt has travelled along a P–T–t path. Its metamorphic assemblage will record some point along its path, but which point will this be? In general, the assemblage records the highest temperature the rock has experienced. This is because metamorphic reactions, like all chemical reactions, speed up exponentially with increased temperature.

● Can you think of any examples of metamorphic reactions that do not occur at peak temperatures?

● Retrograde reactions occur during cooling as evidenced by biotite being replaced by chlorite.

Retrograde reactions are favoured by slow cooling and by fluid infiltration during cooling. Fortunately, many metamorphic rocks show no textural evidence for retrograde reactions and their assemblages probably do reflect equilibrium that is reached at, or close to, the highest metamorphic grade they have experienced.

If we join up the pressure–temperature estimates from several different rocks exhumed within an orogen on a pressure–temperature diagram, do such lines record ancient geotherms? If so, can we reconstruct geotherms precisely by detailed studies of mineral assemblages? The answer to these questions is important because the shape of ancient geotherms can reveal not only the mechanism responsible for the geotherm, but also the rates at which orogenic events have taken place.

Let us consider for a moment how the different rocks in a series of metamorphic zones might have reached their individual metamorphic maxima resulting from crustal thickening by thrusting (Section 6.1.2). Immediately after thrusting had stopped, each rock would be at its maximum depth. The temperature of each rock would therefore lie on a transient geotherm of some kind.

🔘 What would be the mechanical response of the thickened crust?

🔘 Crustal thickening would create a negative gravitational anomaly. This is relieved by isostatic uplift. Erosion of the surface would expose rocks buried in the pile. Every rock would rise to higher levels and lower pressures.

Throughout this process of exhumation, heating would continue at deeper levels due to heat production in the thickened crust. Some of this heat would be lost by cooling nearer the surface, because of conduction. So each rock would describe a P–T–t loop characteristic of that stratum of the crustal pile. The temperature of each stratum would rise for as long as heat production outweighed heat loss to

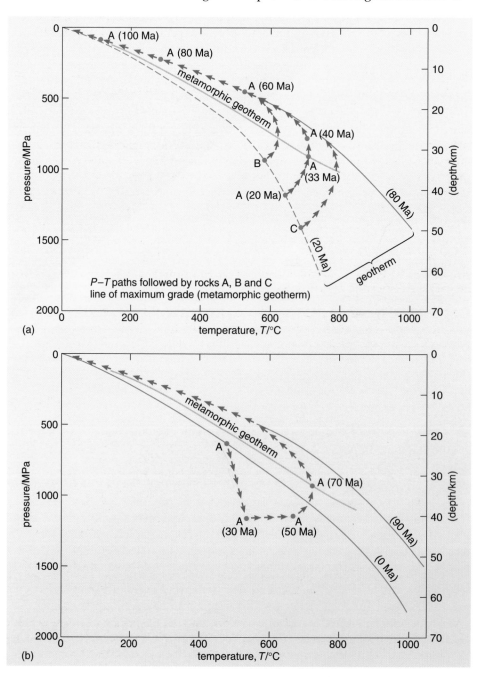

Figure 6.23 Evolution of individual rocks in P–T space during a hypothetical history of burial, radioactive heating and exhumation. All times are given in Ma after crustal thickening occurred. (a) For instantaneous thrusting. (b) For homogeneous thickening over 30 Ma. The solid orange line (metamorphic geotherm) joins the thermal maxima of all rocks in the pile.

the surface. The rock would continue to rise to the surface after it passed its thermal maximum, but now it could be cooled by surface heat loss. The final uplift path is along the steady-state geotherm.

An example of such a thermal evolution is illustrated in Figure 6.23a. The development of P–T conditions of one particular rock (A) is traced at 20, 33, 40, 60, 80 and 100 Ma after its rapid burial by tectonic means. These values have been determined mathematically using equations such as Equation 6.1 (Section 6.1.1). It is assumed that exhumation began 20 Ma after burial, by which time the transient geotherm on which A, B and C lie had developed and any saw-tooth geotherm due to thrusting (Figure 6.8) had decayed. At 20 Ma, rock A was at a temperature of 625 °C at a depth of 42 km (1200 MPa). Pressure gradually decreased with exhumation and the rock heated up towards the steady-state geotherm faster than heat could be conducted away. At 33 Ma, a maximum of 720 °C was reached at a depth of 31 km (900 MPa). By this time, heating from heat production was balanced by cooling from conduction. Thereafter, as rock A continued to be exhumed, its temperature began to wane. The P–T path eventually merged with the steady-state geotherm developed after 80 Ma. By 115 Ma, rock A had reached the surface. Figure 6.24a also shows how P and T varied with time for rocks B and C.

Performing the same exercise for rocks B and C, which were originally buried to different depths, allows the P–T conditions at which they experienced their peak metamorphic temperatures to be predicted.

Since metamorphic assemblages are usually preserved from the peak metamorphic temperatures of their P–T–t path, the geotherm obtained from mineral studies would look very much like the orange line in Figure 6.23a. It is important to note that this does not represent any geotherm which existed during the orogenic event. Although the climaxes for A, B and C lay on transient geotherms, the peaks were reached at different times. This is because the deeper the rock was in the crust, the longer it took to reach its maximum grade. This can be seen from Figure 6.23a, where rock C must be uplifted about 15 km before reaching peak metamorphism but rock B only about 5 km. The line joining the maxima is the **metamorphic geotherm** and is not the same as any of the geotherms used to generate Figure 6.23.

So far, we have considered the thermal consequences of crustal thickening by rapid thrusting. This model was developed in the Outer Zone of the Alps, where thickening was accomplished largely by thrust tectonics, but how would the

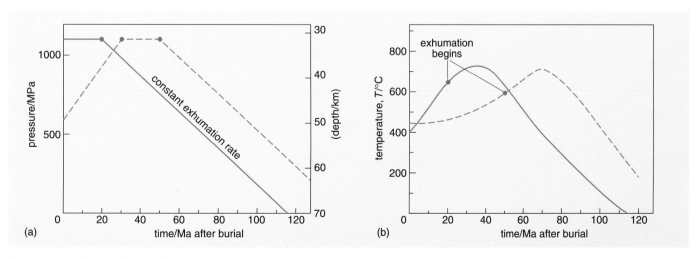

Figure 6.24 Graphs derived from Figure 6.23. (a) Change of pressure (depth) with time for rock A. Note that erosion begins at 20 Ma after burial and is at a constant rate. (b) Change of temperature of rock A with time. Thickening by thrust tectonics is shown as a solid line and homogeneous thickening is shown as a dashed line.

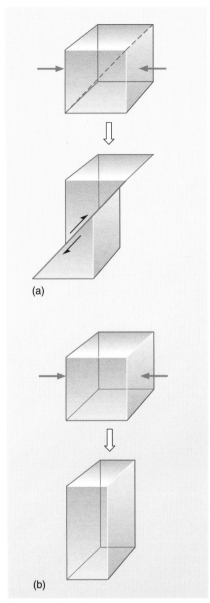

Figure 6.25 The geometry of two styles of thickening. (a) The cube increases its height by 50% due to thrusting. (b) The same effect as a result of homogeneous thickening.

model differ if the crust were thickened over a longer period of time or at deeper crustal levels by ductile deformation? Thickening of this type can most easily be modelled by assuming that the crust thickens by **homogeneous thickening** which means that the vertical dimension expands whilst conserving the volume of rock (Figure 6.25). The assumption of homogeneous thickening on a crustal scale greatly simplifies the mathematics required for thermal modelling. However, it should be remembered that such models do not take into account real structural geometries. On a local scale, any thickening will involve faulting and folding as described in Sections 2 and 3, but it is assumed in homogeneous thickening models that such structures do not affect the thermal evolution of the crust.

As for any model, we have to make some assumptions about starting conditions. Let us assume that the crust doubled in thickness over a period of 30 Ma, and that exhumation began 20 Ma after thickening had ceased. Both crustal thickening and exhumation are assumed to occur at a constant rate through time. The results are shown in Figure 6.23b. Rock A at a depth of 20 km sits on the steady-state geotherm before thickening (0 Ma). Thickening occurs over 30 Ma during which there is an increase in pressure due to the doubling of the initial depth. After 30 Ma, the transient geotherm begins to relax. Some 20 Ma later, uplift will begin so that a drop in pressure and an increase in temperature due to thermal relaxation occur together. At about 70 Ma, the metamorphic grade has reached its peak, and thereafter rock A cools as it moves towards the surface. The $P–T–t$ path joins the steady-state geotherm around 90 Ma after thickening began.

You can see from Figure 6.23b that the metamorphic geotherm for homogeneous thickening has much the same shape as that for the thrust tectonic model. In contrast, the timing of events after thickening started is quite different.

> **Question 6.10** From Figure 6.24, describe the difference in (a) the variation in pressure with time and (b) the variation in temperature with time between the two models for crustal thickening (thrusting and homogeneous thickening). In each case, it is assumed that exhumation began 20 Ma after the crust had doubled in thickness.

Figure 6.23 illustrates thermal relaxation of a transient geotherm from two models of crustal thickening. The line joining $P–T$ maxima in either case is almost linear. In contrast, Figure 6.26 shows a transient geotherm due to the emplacement of an intrusion in the lower crust and compares this to a hypothetical steady-state geotherm.

● Consider the likely peak temperature of rocks from different depths on Figure 6.26 after the end of convective heating. What will the line joining climax $P–T$s look like?

● In this case, all rocks will cool towards the steady-state and so the line joining climax $P–T$s will be the same shape as the transient geotherm — curved line (2) on Figure 6.27, with rapid increase in P at high T.

Figure 6.27 summarizes the theoretical shapes of metamorphic geotherms resulting from crustal thickening and from convection. It illustrates an important relationship between the metamorphic geotherm and the way in which the crust is heated during orogeny. Remember that these metamorphic geotherms are probably all that can be recovered from studying metamorphic assemblages. Indeed although metamorphic minerals do not provide direct evidence for ancient geotherms, they do provide information on the relationship between deformation and thermal evolution, on the rates of uplift relative to thermal relaxation, and on the contributions of conduction and convection to heat flow during orogeny.

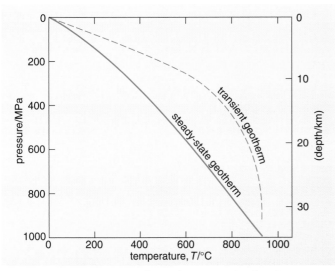
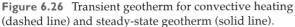

Figure 6.26 Transient geotherm for convective heating (dashed line) and steady-state geotherm (solid line).

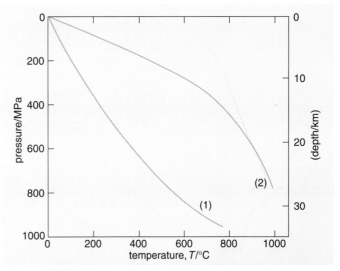

Figure 6.27 Maximum T plotted against P (metamorphic geotherms) for (1) crustal thickening, (2) convection.

6.4   Summary of Section 6

- The steady-state geotherm ($\Delta T / \Delta z$) is related to heat flow (q) and thermal conductivity (k) by the equation

$$q = k \frac{\Delta T}{\Delta z}$$

  Its shape depends largely on the distribution of heat-producing elements in the crust.

- During an orogeny, crustal thickening perturbs the steady-state geotherm into a transient geotherm. The shape of the transient geotherm is initially controlled by the geological process responsible for the perturbation, but in all cases the transient geotherm will relax by conduction towards the steady-state geotherm.

- Thrust tectonics will initially result in a saw-tooth geotherm. Only rapid exhumation will preserve the inverted metamorphic gradient that results from such a geotherm.

- Textures in metamorphic rocks can provide evidence for the timing of metamorphism relative to deformation.

- The nature and compositions of minerals that co-exist in a metamorphic rock result from a series of mineral reactions. The resulting mineral equilibria may be useful as a geothermometer or a geobarometer depending on the gradient of the reaction in pressure–temperature space.

- The pressure–temperature plot derived from several metamorphic rocks in a mountain belt defines the metamorphic geotherm. This plot joins the pressure–temperature conditions experienced by each rock at the time of its maximum metamorphic grade.

- Thermal models can predict the time interval that occurs between deformation and metamorphism at a given depth.

- The shape of the metamorphic geotherm can distinguish between heating from crustal thickening and heating from magmatic intrusion.

Objectives for Section 6

Now that you have completed this Section, you should be able to:

6.1   Understand the meaning of all the terms printed in **bold**.

6.2   Explain the distinction between steady-state and transient geotherms and the geological processes that control them.

6.3   Sketch the shapes of transient geotherms due to conductive and convective heat transfer to the Earth's crust, and explain their significance.

6.4   Identify common metamorphic minerals in pelitic rocks using a polarizing microscope.

6.5   Recognize textural evidence in thin sections or photomicrographs for the timing of growth of metamorphic minerals relative to the deformation of the rock.

6.6   Discuss, using sketches of geotherms, the process of thermal relaxation from transient geotherms to the steady-state, and relate this evolution to the mineralogical record of metamorphism.

Now try the following questions to test your understanding of Section 6.

Question 6.11   What geological processes are responsible for (a) heating and (b) cooling of crustal rocks? In each case, indicate whether heat transfer results from conduction or convection.

Question 6.12   At a rock outcrop, the mineral assemblage is noted from inspection with a hand-lens. What further information would you require to assess (a) the pressure and temperature at which the mineral assemblage formed and (b) the relationship between regional deformation and mineral growth?

Question 6.13   The chlorite–biotite–garnet–staurolite–kyanite Barrow zones from the Grampian phase of the Caledonian orogeny provide mineral assemblages which lie on an approximately linear array when plotted on a P–T diagram. Summarize the argument that this line does *not* represent either an ancient steady-state geotherm or a transient geotherm which existed during mountain building.

a) i) magmatic intrusion (convection)
ii) fluid flow (convection)
iii) Radioactive decay (conduction)

b) i) exhumation (conduction)
ii) Nappes (thrusting) conduction)

6:12
a) The composition of minerals and the P-T stability of the mineral
b) The shape and growth history of the minerals show timing relative to deformation

7 The Himalaya and Tibet: a case study of collision

7.1 Introduction

The Greater Himalayan ranges and the Tibetan Plateau form a vast mountainous region north of the Indian subcontinent (Figure 7.1). In the nineteenth century, explorers were concerned with the region for strategic reasons — the mountains formed the boundary between the British and Russian Empires. Topographic mapping of the mountain ranges led to more academic research. These studies provided the framework for early recognition of gravity anomalies associated with high topographic elevations and hence were pivotal in understanding the distribution of mass below mountain belts. Later, the surveys gradually pieced together the geology of the region, with scientific teams attached to mountaineering expeditions often working in extremely harsh conditions. However, the main impetus for geological study came in the 1960s when it was recognized that the Himalayan mountains formed from the collision and continued convergence between the Indian subcontinent and the rest of central Asia. That this overall plate convergence is still operating is indicated not only by the sheer size of the mountains, where uplift rates greatly exceed those of erosion, but also by the abundant landslips and widespread seismicity.

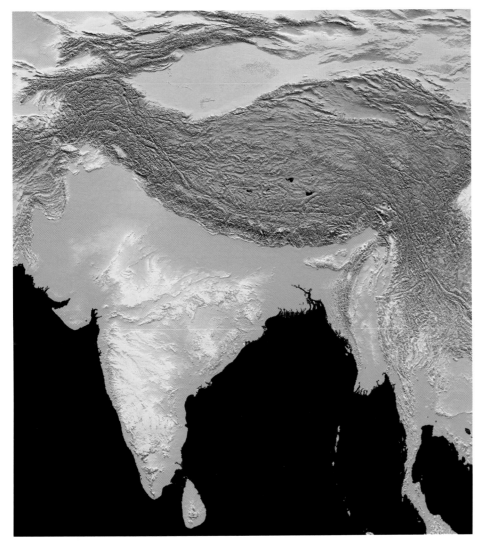

Figure 7.1 Digital elevation map for southern Asia: green = 0–500 m; yellow = 500–2000 m; brown = 2000–4000 m; red = 4000–5000 m; grey = >5000 m.

The Himalaya stretch from the Indus in northern Pakistan, across northern India, Nepal and Bhutan to the Tsangpo gorge in south-east Tibet (Figure 7.2). They form a narrow, arcuate mountain range that should not be confused with the Tibetan Plateau, a broad highland region over 2000 km across from the Himalaya in the south to the deserts of central Asia in the north. The average elevation of this plateau is 5000 m and, although it never reaches the extreme altitudes of the highest Himalayan peaks (> 8000 m), it is the largest and highest plateau on Earth (Figure 7.1). Geological knowledge of Tibet is not yet as detailed as that of the Himalaya because of its inaccessibility. But we do know that, although Tibet's elevation can be related to the same collision event that was responsible for uplift of the Himalaya, the lithosphere beneath the Tibetan Plateau and that beneath the Himalaya have been thickened by quite distinct mechanisms.

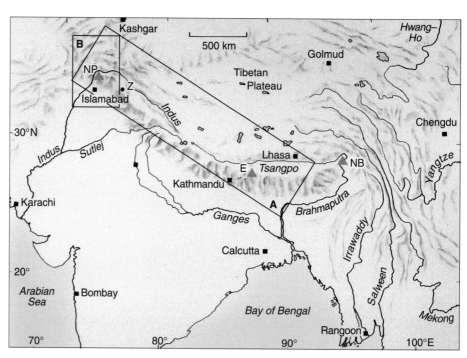

Figure 7.2   The geography of southern Asia showing location of Figures 7.5 (box A) and 7.1.1 (box B) in *Workbook 4*. Z = Zanskar; E = Everest; NP = Nanga Parbat; NB = Namcha Barwa.

India and Eurasia initially collided during the Paleogene (Figure 7.3a,b), but convergence continues to this day and so Tibet and the Himalaya record events over 50 million years of Earth history, providing geologists with a natural laboratory for studying collision tectonics. In this Section, we shall unravel the anatomy of the orogen in order to understand the processes responsible for its formation. We shall focus particularly on the structural, metamorphic and igneous evidence provided by the rocks themselves.

We shall start this investigation with the suture zone itself (Section 7.2) and the evidence preserved in the igneous rocks of the region for the nature and timing of the collision (Section 7.3). We shall then investigate the tectonics of the Tibetan Plateau and the Himalaya in turn (Sections 7.4, 7.5). Finally, we shall turn to neotectonics from the western Himalaya of northern Pakistan for a unique example of active mountain building (Section 7.6).

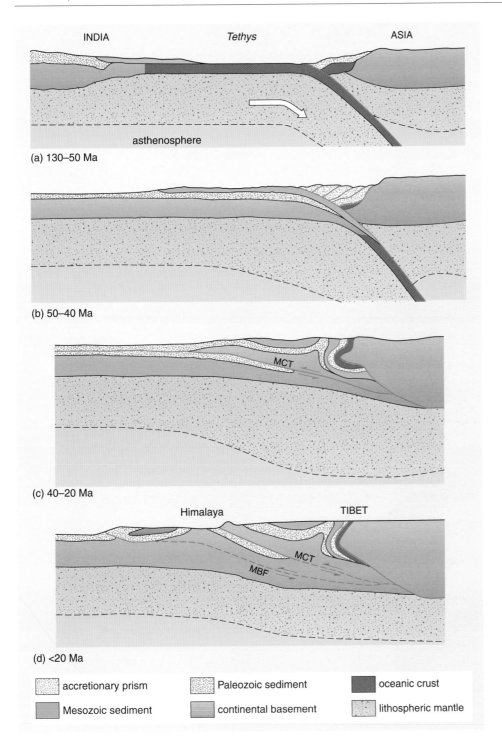

Figure 7.3 Four stages in the India–Asia collision. (a) Subduction of Tethys before collision. (b) Initial collision of continental lithospheres with obduction of the ophiolite and deformation in the suture zone. (c) Thickening of the crust south of the suture by thrusting on the Main Central Thrust (MCT). (d) Continued thickening by thrusting on more southerly faults such as the Main Boundary Fault (MBF).

7.2 The Tethyan Suture zone

Within the Tsangpo Valley of southern Tibet (Figure 7.4) lies a series of ophiolitic fragments that can be traced in a discontinuous line for thousands of kilometres from Assam in the east to Pakistan in the west (Figure 7.5). The recognition of ophiolites within an orogenic belt is important because these represent the remnants of the oceanic lithosphere that has been subducted. Ophiolites in a collision zone are initially obducted (Figure 7.3b), but during the collision process are strongly deformed and may be displaced from the initial site of the suture by strike–slip or thrust tectonics.

Figure 7.4 The Tethyan Suture zone in the Tsangpo Valley, southern Tibet, looking north. The rounded hills in the foreground are serpentinites from the ophiolite sequence. The rugged hills in the background are granites from the Trans-Himalayan batholith.

How would you verify that a zone of ophiolite fragments found within continental crust marks an ancient suture zone which separated two plates or terranes?

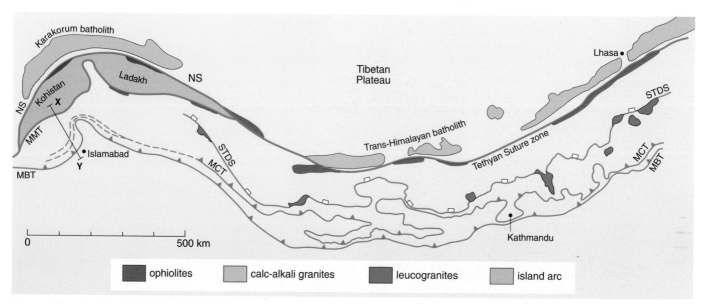

Figure 7.5 Geological sketch map across the Himalaya and southern Tibet showing distribution of plutonic rocks and major thrusts. STDS = South Tibetan Detachment System; NS = Northern Suture; MMT = Main Mantle Thrust; MCT = Main Central Thrust; and MBT = Main Boundary Thrust. X–Y = section of Figure 7.38. For location see Figure 7.2.

If the zone of ophiolites bounds two terranes which were once widely displaced, a study of the stratigraphy on either side of the ophiolite line might reveal contrasting sedimentary patterns. Equally, geochemical studies of igneous rocks might reveal contrasting properties of the crust through which the magmas have evolved or paleomagnetic studies might reveal contrasting pre-collision drift histories. Moreover, if the ophiolite remained in the suture zone, it should be associated with continental margin sediments, deformed by the collision (Figure 7.3).

In the case of southern Tibet, contrasting geochemical and sedimentological features are found either side of a belt of strongly deformed continental sediments onto which the ophiolite has been obducted. These ophiolites *are* therefore thought to mark the boundary between India and Asia and the closure of the Tethys Ocean. They define a line which is known as the Tethyan Suture zone. The sequence of events that led up to the incorporation of fragments of the Tethyan ocean basin in the suture zone are illustrated in Figure 7.3c and d.

Question 7.1 Given your knowledge of the subduction of Tethys, what types of old continental margin lie on either side of the Tethyan Suture zone?

The exposed ophiolite fragments along the Tsangpo river include serpentinites, banded gabbros, sheeted dykes and pillow lavas (Figure 7.6); in fact, virtually a complete sequence through oceanic crust. U–Pb dating of zircons from the gabbros indicates an age of 120 Ma, but this merely tells us when that part of the ocean crust was formed at a mid-ocean ridge. If we want to know when collision occurred, all we can say from this date is that collision must have been after that time.

Figure 7.6 Pillow lavas from the Tethyan Suture zone of southern Tibet, now at an altitude of ~4000 m.

By dating sediments over which the ophiolite has been obducted, we obtain a maximum age for obduction (i.e. the ophiolite could not have been obducted before the sediments were deposited). A minimum age can be obtained by dating the continental sediments which overlie the obducted ophiolite.

The youngest sediments which pre-date obduction are marine sandstones, limestones and shales of Paleogene age. These are the youngest part of the old passive continental margin of India. They are overlain by Neogene conglomerates that were deposited by early Himalayan rivers and post-date obduction. The metamorphic grade is low, with the post-obduction deformation generating thrusts which cut the conglomerates. The faunal evidence suggests that final obduction onto continental crust occurred during the Mid or Late Paleogene (52–38 Ma).

As we trace the ophiolite fragments west, we find a bifurcation into two possible suture zones in the western Himalaya (Figure 7.5). The southern ophiolites delineate the Main Mantle Thrust (MMT for short) and the northern strand (the Northern Suture, NS) bounds the Kohistan terrane, a fragment (which includes Ladakh to the east) with a quite separate history to India or the Asian continental mass to the north.

7.2.1 The Main Mantle Thrust

In the western Himalaya, the suture zone between Kohistan and India is a major zone of intense ductile deformation, tectonically equivalent to the Tethyan Suture of the central Himalaya. Like ophiolite fragments from the Tethyan Suture zone, the ophiolites of the MMT were obducted during the Paleogene.

The map pattern of the MMT (Figure 7.5) forms a prominent loop. This is termed the Nanga Parbat syntaxis. Syntaxes are regions where mountain ranges merge together; in this case it is where the Himalaya converge with the Asian ranges of the Karakorum and Hindu Kush. We will examine the origin of the Nanga Parbat syntaxis later in this Block. For now, however, we can concentrate on the excellent structures exposed in the steep gorge walls of the Indus and use these to establish the nature of the MMT.

Activity 7.1

Now attempt the video-based activity on the Karakorum geotraverse and the MMT. You should take about 90 minutes to do this Activity.

From this Activity, it is clear that the MMT is a remarkable structure in that it is a rare demonstration of the correlation between field observations and regional plate movements. Kohistan has overthrust Indian continental crust — the equivalent to northward-directed subduction. So, we have an indication of how the Himalayan crust began to deform following the closure of Tethys. Both the Tethys Ocean (the oceanic part of the Indian Plate) and the attached Indian continent were overthrust by the Kohistan arc in a broadly southward direction.

Ophiolitic sutures are not the only indication of old subduction zones. High P–low T metamorphism as indicated by blueschist-facies assemblages might be expected in Himalayan rocks within the suture zone. Excellent blueschist exposures (characterized by the blue amphibole, glaucophane) are found south of the MMT in the western Himalaya. A 3 km-wide belt of blueschists provides mineral ages of 80–90 Ma, suggesting a pre-collision, syn-subduction origin.

⬤ What explanation could there be for the observation that blueschists are not common in the central section of the Tethyan Suture, and that they have been found along less than 0.5% of its entire length?

⬤ High *P*–low *T* metamorphic rocks require unusually rapid uplift in order to preserve blueschist-facies assemblages (Section 6.2.3). If rocks from the central Himalaya were exhumed more slowly, blueschist facies minerals would not be preserved.

7.2.2 The Northern Suture of Kohistan

The Northern Suture represents the docking of the Kohistan terrane onto the southern edge of the Asian landmass. From stratigraphic and radiometric dating of sediments and late intrusions which cross the suture, the docking event has been dated as late Cretaceous in age.

⬤ From the Video Band *Karakorum geotraverse*, is the Northern Suture of Kohistan associated with significant thrusting?

⬤ The suture zone contains rocks at greenschist facies and the deformation, although locally intense, is characterized by upright folds and cleavages. There is no sign of significant thrusting.

The Northern Suture is marked by a narrow belt of mixed sedimentary and volcanic blocks caught up in a slatey matrix. Some of these blocks are as large as several kilometres across. This style of sedimentation suggests significant slopes and areas of tectonic instability such as are found at ocean trenches. Similar rock assemblages, known as mélanges, are found along the west coast of North America and in trenches off Japan. In the Northern Suture, the only evidence for the narrow ocean basin which separated Kohistan from the Karakorum in Mid-Cretaceous times is a few kilometres of mélange.

An important conclusion arising from the Northern Suture is that the actual collision between crustal fragments need not produce massive overthrust tectonics and crustal shortening. Indeed, there is no evidence for the region being a mountain range in late Cretaceous times. Similarly, in some older examples of mountain building such as during the Paleozoic history of the British Caledonides, the sites of major plate boundaries are not marked by belts of intense metamorphism and deformation which typify Alpine-type mountain belts. The implication is that mountain belts and the substantial crustal shortening which build them are not a necessary consequence of the initial impact but rather are a consequence of the plate convergence which continues *after* collision.

7.2.3 Summary of Section 7.2

• The Tethyan Suture zone is marked by a chain of ophiolite fragments that represent fragments of the Tethys oceanic crust that were obducted between 52 and 38 Ma.

• These fragments have not been significantly displaced since obduction and hence mark the boundary between the Indian and Eurasian Plates.

• Within the westernmost region of the Tethyan Suture zone (MMT), shear criteria record a movement sense that documents large scale plate movement between Kohistan and the Indian Plate.

• The Northern Suture is a narrow zone of deformed low-grade metamorphic rocks with no evidence of overthrusting.

7.3   Convergence and magmatism

The subduction of large volumes of oceanic lithosphere as implied by the disappearance of Tethys must have induced voluminous magmatism. Since the Tethyan Suture marks the join between India and pre-collision Asia along a northward-dipping subduction zone, we would expect large tracts of subduction-related magmatism to occur at some distance to the north of the suture.

In fact, the southern edge of Tibet is marked by a vast igneous arc which stretches from the Karakorum in the west to the eastern Himalaya and Assam over 3000 km away. The plutonic component of this igneous arc is known as the Trans-Himalayan batholith (Figures 7.4, 7.5). Because of the remoteness of much of its exposure, only a few areas of the batholith have been studied in any detail.

7.3.1   The Trans-Himalayan batholith

The Trans-Himalayan batholith of southern Tibet is about 50 km wide and is characterized by discrete plutons of biotite and hornblende granodiorites and granites, with lesser volumes of tonalites and diorites. Plutonics of intermediate composition (tonalites and diorites) were emplaced earlier in the igneous history, often occurring as xenoliths within more-evolved plutons (Figure 7.7). Geochemical analysis of these plutonic rocks indicates a calc-alkaline suite, indistinguishable from rocks found in the Andean coastal batholith.

Figure 7.7   Xenoliths of diorite within a granite pluton from the Trans-Himalayan batholith, south of Lhasa.

The earliest magmatism recorded in this region of the belt is about 100 Ma and it continued until 40 Ma, more or less continuously, so that the igneous evidence suggests that subduction-related magmatism continued from the Mid-Cretaceous until the Paleogene collision.

Question 7.2 How does this span of magmatism correlate with the reconstruction of plate movements deduced from ocean floor magnetic anomalies (Figure 1.6)?

The calc-alkaline plutons of the Trans-Himalayan batholith intrude strongly deformed Mesozoic sediments, and also a thick volcanic cover in southern Tibet which is Paleogene in age (about 50–60 Ma). Altogether, the Paleogene volcanic succession is about 2000 m thick in the Lhasa area and is dominated by andesitic lavas, with dacitic and rhyolitic pyroclastics becoming more abundant towards the top of the succession.

The volcanics unconformably overlie folded sediments, known from fossil evidence to be Upper Cretaceous in age (Figure 7.8). The first geologists to map these rocks assumed that the sediments were folded during the collision between India and Asia and so inferred that the volcanics were Neogene in age. More recently the volcanics were dated isotopically. The results indicated an age of 60 Ma, pre-dating collision by about 10 Ma.

Figure 7.8 Unconformity between folded Cretaceous sediments and 60 Ma volcanics from southern Tibet.

This result suggests that the sediments were folded *during* subduction of oceanic lithosphere. Folding does not necessarily imply continental collision; for example, the sedimentary cover of the Andean batholith has been folded during deformation at an active continental margin.

As we trace the Trans-Himalayan batholith westwards, the simple relationship between a single suture and a magmatic arc is complicated by the fact that the suture splits into two strands, the Northern Suture and the Main Mantle Thrust. To the north of the Northern Suture, the magmatic arc is known as the **Karakorum batholith** (Figure 7.5). Like the Trans-Himalayan batholith in the Lhasa region, this is a composite, largely plutonic, complex including granites, granodiorites, tonalites and diorites of calc-alkaline compositions which intrude sediments of Mesozoic and Late Paleozoic age. However, the age relations are different here.

The oldest units of the batholith are about 110 Ma old but there appears to be a hiatus between 70 Ma and about 50 Ma. The Karakorum batholith was emplaced almost entirely during the Cretaceous, but the composite plutons are cut by

Tertiary granite sheets (Figure 7.9). Many of the plutons are strongly affected by Late Cretaceous deformation which resulted from closure of the Northern Suture. But we know from the earlier discussion that the Northern Suture bounds the Kohistan terrane to the south and Karakorum to the north, so the subduction related to the closure of the ocean basin between these two terranes ended with their collision about 70 to 80 Ma ago. The younger granite sheets must result from a more recent tectonic event to which we shall return shortly.

Figure 7.9 Tertiary granite sheets cutting diorite from the Karakorum batholith.

7.3.2 The Kohistan island arc

The Kohistan terrane lies south of the Northern Suture. Kohistan is composed almost entirely of igneous rocks with the shallower levels exposed to the north and deeper levels to the south (Figure 7.10). Mid-Cretaceous shales and limestones, typical of marine deposition, are found in northern exposures of the arc. Beneath these lies a 3-km sequence of volcanics which is Mid to Late Cretaceous in age.

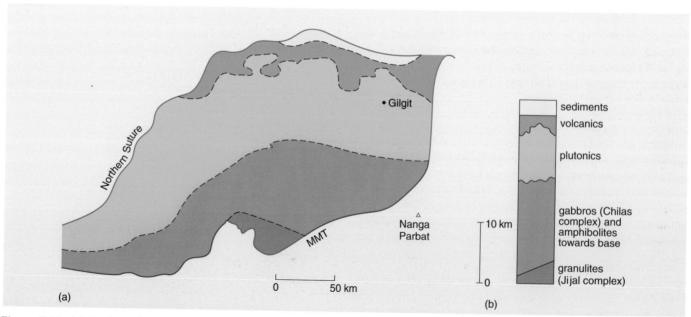

Figure 7.10 (a) Geological sketch map of the Kohistan terrane (see Figure 7.5 for location). (b) Schematic vertical section through the Kohistan arc.

Table 7.1 Compositions of magmatic rocks from the Himalaya. Oxides in wt %; trace elements in ppm. All iron calculated as FeO.

	Lhasa volcanics (60–50 Ma)		Lhasa plutonics (60–50 Ma)		Karakorum plutonics (110–90 Ma)		Kohistan volcanics (100–65 Ma)			Kohistan plutonics (100–70 Ma) (70–40 Ma)		Leucogranite (20 Ma)
	LV1	LV2	LP1	LP2	KA1	KA2	KV1	KV2	KV3	KP1	KP2	LG1
Oxides (wt. %)												
SiO$_2$	60.20	67.40	65.96	73.76	63.30	69.50	45.81	49.15	59.04	69.84	73.87	73.65
TiO$_2$	0.80	0.37	0.75	0.22	0.80	0.40	0.69	0.61	0.39	0.26	0.17	0.10
Al$_2$O$_3$	16.50	15.10	15.41	14.20	16.50	14.70	15.22	13.07	15.52	15.74	14.01	14.90
FeO	5.86	1.70	4.98	1.73	5.40	2.10	8.94	8.36	3.99	3.14	1.38	0.80
MnO	0.15	0.04	0.07	0.03	0.10	0.10	0.17	0.16	0.14	0.06	0.04	0.01
MgO	4.26	0.70	1.56	0.61	2.70	0.70	7.05	11.65	2.40	1.39	0.30	0.10
CaO	7.06	5.00	4.17	1.71	5.50	1.70	12.08	8.70	5.82	3.58	1.55	0.49
Na$_2$O	2.56	4.78	3.44	3.00	3.00	4.00	2.96	1.82	3.84	5.10	3.45	4.05
K$_2$O	0.80	1.06	3.16	5.53	2.00	5.00	0.05	0.83	1.49	0.85	5.05	4.60
P$_2$O$_5$	0.13	0.10	0.18	0.05	0.20	0.20	0.19	0.14	0.23	0.04	0.05	0.10
Trace elements (ppm)												
Rb	18	57	108	137	78	234	4	13	40	8	202	267
Sr	833	456	304	242	387	796	247	167	239	170	249	76
Zr	146	105	208	99	148	244	35	31	125	74	128	43

Early flows from the volcanics form pillow lavas with compositions similar to that of sample KV1 in Table 7.1. Later flows are more varied in composition (KV2, KV3 in Table 7.1).

> **Question 7.3** Using the analyses in Table 7.1 and geochemical plots TiO$_2$ vs. Zr, K$_2$O vs. SiO$_2$ and FeO/MgO vs. SiO$_2$ from Block 3, what can you say about the evolution of magmas from KV1, KV2 and KV3 in terms of the tectonic environment in which they erupted?

The sediments and the volcanics are believed to represent the upper two lithologies of a complete section through an island arc, now exposed on its side in the Kohistan terrane (Figure 7.10). The volcanics are intruded by plutons with a range of compositions. Earlier intrusions are mainly gabbros, diorite and tonalites of tholeiitic composition, emplaced around 100 Ma ago (e.g. KP1, Table 7.1). More recent intrusions emplaced between 70 and 40 Ma are more siliceous and are dominated by calc-alkaline granodiorites and granites (KP2). They also reflect magmatism formed within a maturing island arc, in which a progressively thickening crust resulted in more granitic magmas. The earlier, more basic, suites result from subduction prior to the closure of the Northern Suture. The younger group results from closure of Tethys after Kohistan had docked onto the Karakorum terrane. Granite sheets, which can be traced north of the Northern Suture into the Karakorum batholith (Figure 7.9), represent the youngest magmatic event of all. Some of these sheets may be as young as 30 Ma.

The increasingly silica-rich magmatism may have resulted from subduction and re-melting of sediments from the continental margin which converged on Kohistan from the south. Alternatively, it may have resulted from increasing fractionation of magmas with time as the island arc evolved.

Question 7.4 How could isotopic studies help you to distinguish between these two possibilities?

Continuing down the sequence of the Kohistan arc (Figure 7.10), extensive stratiform cumulates, known as the Chilas complex, are exposed. This complex, which is 300 km long and more than 8 km thick, is made up of gabbros and ultramafic rocks. Particularly impressive are the rhythmically layered cumulates which show graded bedding, and syn-sedimentation faults illustrated in the Video Band '*Karakorum geotraverse*'. Zircons taken from the Chilas gabbros are 80–90 Ma old, so the cumulates could have crystallized in the magma chambers which fed the lavas and plutons exposed to the north.

The basal lithology exposed in the Kohistan island arc is a high-pressure metamorphic equivalent of the Chilas complex. Typically, ultramafic rocks such as peridotite are interlayered with garnet–pyroxene–plagioclase assemblages. These rocks have a similar composition to gabbros in the Chilas complex, but have been metamorphosed in the granulite facies. Isotopic ages suggest that the garnet in the granulites was formed around 90 Ma ago. The metamorphic grade increases with depth throughout the Kohistan island arc, but it is only in these basal garnet granulites (known as the Jijal complex) that hydrous minerals like amphibole become unstable due to the higher temperatures. Studies of the metamorphic mineral assemblages indicate pressures of 800–1200 MPa at temperatures of 800 °C so, if the garnet granulite comes from the base of the island arc, it must have been at least 30 km thick, similar in thickness to normal continental crust. This suggests that, by 90 Ma, Kohistan was a mature island arc.

Towards the base of the Kohistan island arc, banded amphibolites and deformed pegmatite sheets provide increasing evidence of deformation (Figure 7.11).

Figure 7.11 Cross-cutting granitic intrusions in banded amphibolites of the lower part of the Kohistan island arc terrane.

Question 7.5 There are two granitic intrusions shown in Figure 7.11. Describe the relationship between deformation and intrusion. Both granitic veins form part of a suite of minor intrusions between 80 and 90 Ma, so what is the age of the deformation?

The field relations along the Karakorum Highway suggest that the lower part of the Kohistan island arc experienced deformation during the magmatic build up — probably at around 80–90 Ma, well before Kohistan collided with India. This is consistent with a model of mature island arcs with hot, deeper levels leading to ductile deformation and gravity spreading.

7.3.3 Summary of Section 7.3

- Subduction at an active continental margin from about 110 Ma is recorded by calc-alkaline plutonic and volcanic rocks from the Karakorum in the west, across southern Tibet and probably over the entire Trans-Himalayan arc.

- In the central Himalaya, calc-alkaline magmatism continued from the Lower Cretaceous to the Paleogene.

- In the western Himalaya, magmatism ceased by about 70 Ma in the Karakorum indicating the docking of the Kohistan terranes along the Northern Suture.

- Tholeiitic magmatism in Kohistan heralded the beginning of an island arc at 100 Ma.

- Kohistan evolved to a mature island arc over 30 km thick, with magmatism continuing with granitic plutonism until 40 Ma.

- In the western Himalaya, the final closure of Tethys is indicated by Paleogene granite sheets in both Kohistan and the Karakorum.

Activity 7.2

Consolidate your knowledge of the timing of magmatic events in the Himalaya by trying Activity 7.2. You should take about 45 minutes to do this Activity.

7.4   Thickening of the Tibetan lithosphere

7.4.1   Introduction

Since collision, the convergence between India and Eurasia must have been accommodated largely by deformation of continental lithosphere because there was no more Tethyan oceanic lithosphere to be subducted. Paleomagnetic data suggest that the southern margin of the Tibetan Plateau, just north of the suture, has moved northwards by about 2000 km relative to the stable part of Eurasia. Shortening across the Himalaya is estimated at 400–500 km since collision. Within the limits of paleomagnetic errors, about 80% of the convergence has been accommodated by deformation in central Asia. How has this been achieved?

7.4.2   The thin viscous sheet model

Figure 7.1 shows much of eastern and central Asia to be characterized by complex knots of mountain ranges, but the largest extent of high elevation is much more simple. The Tibetan Plateau has a remarkably uniform elevation of around 5 km above sea-level. Geophysical studies confirm that this reflects a greatly increased crustal thickness (on average about 90 km thick) with topography generated as an isostatic consequence. This raises an important geodynamic question: is there a limit to the amount of crustal thickening that can be achieved?

To tackle the problem, Phil England and Dan McKenzie of Oxford and Cambridge Universities developed a model for thickening continental lithosphere. To simplify things, England and McKenzie assumed the deformation to be homogenous — i.e. not 'controlled' by faults. This allowed them to treat the lithosphere as a **thin viscous sheet**. Despite the great thickness of the Tibetan lithosphere, the width of the plateau is an order of magnitude greater than its lithospheric thickness. Their model predicted that a viscous sheet with the dimensions of the Tibetan lithosphere would thicken up under compression to reach a critical value (65–80 km), at which point the buoyancy forces of the thickened lithosphere balance those of the compression. Greater thicknesses would be unstable, resulting in lateral spreading. The actual thickness achieved will depend on the effective viscosity — and hence the thermal structure — of the deformed continental lithosphere, together with the magnitude of the compressive stress applied across the orogen. With continued convergence, the deformation zone will migrate outwards from the previously thickened lithosphere. The model predicts that (i) the Tibetan lithosphere will thicken progressively from south to north and (ii) the lithosphere will eventually collapse by gravity spreading in the central parts of the plateau with active compression around its flanks.

It should be possible to test this second prediction with reference to present-day seismicity. Figure 7.12 is a map illustrating fault-plane solutions for shallow to intermediate depth earthquakes across the Tibetan Plateau.

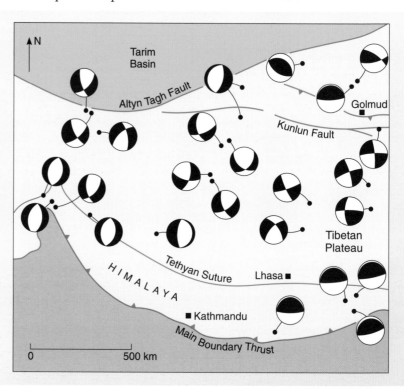

Figure 7.12 Fault-plane solutions for earthquakes across the Tibetan Plateau and the Himalaya.

Box 7.1 Fault-plane solutions

Fault-plane solutions are a graphical means of distinguishing compressional zones, represented by shaded sectors, from extensional or dilational zones, represented by unornamented sectors. The boundaries between the zones on each solution represent the fault plane and the auxiliary plane. Without additional information (e.g. a fault at the surface), it is not possible from these solutions to determine which is the fault plane and which is the auxiliary plane. It is however possible to distinguish between fault types. Quartered fault plane solutions are diagnostic of strike–slip on steep faults. In contrast, the 'eye-shaped' solutions are indicative of dip–slip on inclined faults. Thrust faults are characterized by the central parts of the solution being in compression while normal faults have dilational centres. Oblique slip faults will be intermediate, showing tendencies toward strike–slip but with the intersection of the two model planes shifted away from the centre of the diagram.

Earthquakes from the central and eastern Himalaya, south of the Tethyan Suture, are represented by four fault-plane solutions. Note that all are thrust sense but from the data alone we cannot say if the thrusts were dipping steeply to the SSE (with shallow-dipping auxiliary planes) or gently dipping to the NNW (with steeply dipping auxiliary planes). Both planes in each diagram have the same E–W or WSW–ENE strike, subparallel to the trend of this part of the Himalaya.

> **Question 7.6** Examine the seismicity patterns across Tibet from Figure 7.12. Identify the principal sites of compressional fault-plane solutions and characterize the style of active deformation in the heart of the plateau. How does this match England and McKenzie's prediction?

7.4.3 Escape tectonics

So far, we have assumed that all post-collision convergence between India and Asia will be accommodated by lithospheric thickening, but this may not be entirely true. A glance at India on the *Geological Map of the World* indicates a series of major faults around the northern and eastern margins of the Tibetan Plateau. Two of these (Altyn Tagh and Kunlun) are marked on Figure 7.12. These faults are linear features, easily visible from satellites (Figure 7.13a). On the ground, they form straight, flat-bottomed valleys ideal for siting the few roads in northern Tibet (Figure 7.13b). Geomorphological studies on these faults indicate quite substantial movement of about 10 mm yr^{-1} during the last 10 000 years, sufficient to allow significant displacement of the lithosphere eastwards over millions of years. This mechanism is called **escape tectonics**, because it allows extrusion of central Asia eastwards towards the free margin of the Pacific Ocean where movement is accommodated by subduction (Figure 7.14).

(a)

(b)

Figure 7.13 (a) Satellite image of the Kunlun Fault in northern Tibet seen as a linear east–west feature, bifurcating towards the east (width of image = 200 km). (b) Ground view of the Kunlun Fault with the Kunlun mountains seen to the north.

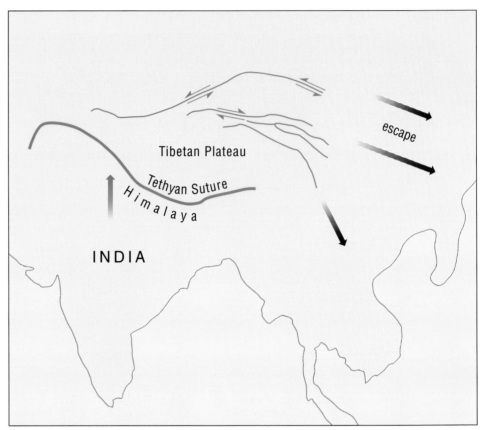

Figure 7.14 Sketch map illustrating the eastward escape of central Asia due to the collision of the Indian continent.

The most important consequence of escape tectonics is that the northward movement of Asia can be accommodated without further thickening or deformation of the Tibetan lithosphere. There is currently debate amongst geologists about the relative contributions of escape tectonics and homogeneous thickening for accommodating the northward migration of India within the Tibetan lithosphere. Numerical modelling, based on the assumption that the Tibetan lithosphere behaves as a thin viscous sheet, suggests that less than 25% of convergence will be accommodated by escape tectonics, the rest being absorbed by lithospheric thickening.

7.4.4 Convective thinning of the lithosphere

The thermal aspects of the viscous sheet model were explored by Dan McKenzie together with Greg Houseman and Peter Molnar (from the Massachusetts Institute of Technology). They realized that greatly thickened continental crust must be underlain by a thickened root of lithospheric mantle. However, lithospheric mantle is colder and denser than the asthenosphere below. Hence, the thickened sub-Tibetan lithosphere will be unstable. After a few million years, the system will begin to convect (Figure 7.15). Their modelling shows that this process will accelerate — with **convective thinning** of the base of the thickened lithosphere.

To understand the consequences of convective thinning for mountain building, we must consider the gravitational balance of the lithosphere. Assuming locally compensated isostasy (i.e. no flexure), the floating rock column will be balanced by buoyant continental crust, held down by the dense **lithospheric mantle root**. You should recall that the maximum elevation of the rock column above the

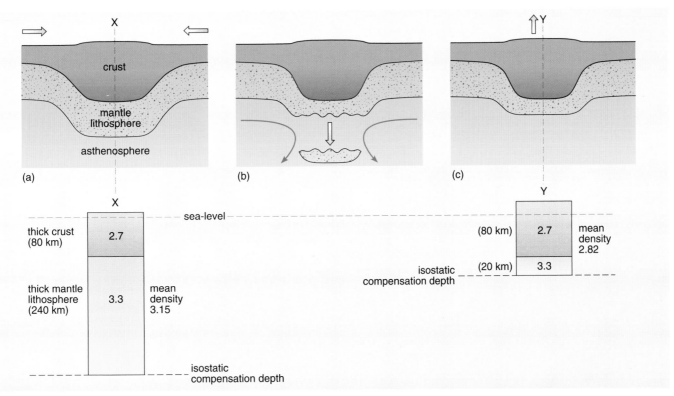

Figure 7.15 The convective thinning model for the uplift of the Tibetan Plateau. (a) Illustrates the thick, post-compression state in cross-section, where a lithospheric rock column (X) is isostatically balanced. (b) Shows in schematic fashion the removal of the dense lithospheric mantle root (replaced by weak asthenosphere). (c) Isostatic uplift of the plateau so that the new rock column (Y) is also in isostatic equilibrium. Thinning raises the isostatic compensation depth in Y, generating uplift. The densities of the crust and mantle lithosphere and the mean value for each column are given in units of $kg\,m^{-3} \times 10^{-3}$.

global reference (e.g. sea-level) depends on the mean density of the column. If we strip off part of the dense mantle root, thus reducing column height, the mean density of the column decreases and the column will be uplifted. Uplift is therefore generated by lithospheric thinning (Figure 7.15) and as a result a time lag is expected between the initiation of thickening and the rapid elevation of the Tibetan Plateau. A testable prediction made by the convective thinning model is therefore that a period of rapid surface uplift occurred some time after the initial collision.

> **Question 7.7** Given the presence of pillow lavas from the ophiolite suite in the Tethyan Suture zone at a present altitude of ~4000 m (Figure 7.6), calculate an average rate for plateau uplift since 50 Ma ago.

Unfortunately, this value is only an average rate. It includes the steady elevation rate over 50 Ma expected from isostastic adjustment to crustal thickening as well as any possible surge in elevation due to convective thinning. More direct evidence comes from detailed analysis of fossil plant leaves in a Neogene sedimentary basin from southern Tibet. Preliminary results suggest that they grew at altitudes of ~3000 m as recently as 15 Ma ago. Since much of the plateau is now at 5000 m, there has been an increase in the rate of uplift over the past 15 Ma ($>0.13\ mm\ yr^{-1}$), long after crustal shortening began 50 Ma ago. Thus, the available evidence is consistent with a time lag between thickening and uplift.

So far we have been discussing a model for Tibetan uplift, but is there any direct evidence for lithospheric thinning? In recent years, geologists have discovered a series of volcanic cones in northern Tibet, erupted in the past

14 Ma (Figures 7.16, 7.17). These Neogene magmas are basaltic andesites that are rich in potassium. Trace elements and isotopic ratios suggest an origin from melting the sub-continental mantle lithosphere. Their origin in a region of thickened crust, well away from subduction zones, has puzzled geologists. Why should basaltic rocks be generated within unusually thickened lithosphere?

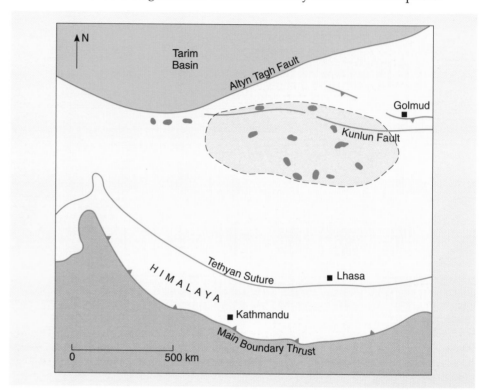

Figure 7.16 Map of the Tibetan Plateau showing the distribution of volcanoes less than 14 Ma old (in red). Dashed line indicates areal extent of slow S-wave velocities.

Figure 7.17 A 4 Ma old cinder cone from northern Tibet.

The answer may lie in the thermal consequences of convective thinning. The geotherm of the lithosphere beneath pre-collision Tibet will be determined by a potential temperature of 1280 °C (Figure 7.18a). Following collision, thickening will result in a shallow geothermal gradient (Figure 7.18b). Remember that here we are considering the entire lithosphere, not just the continental crust. Rapid

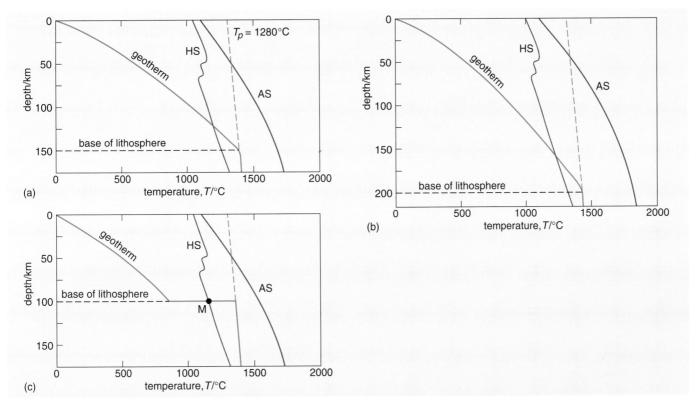

Figure 7.18 Three stages in the thermal evolution of the Tibetan lithosphere. (a) The initial pre-collision geotherm for a lithosphere 150 km thick. (b) The geotherm following homogeneous thickening to 200 km. (c) The geotherm following convective thinning to 100 km. The hydrous solidus (HS) is now crossed at M where melting occurs. AS = anhydrous solidus.

removal of the lithospheric root results in a stepped geotherm which intersects the volatile-enriched solidus at M (Figure 7.18c). In other words, the removal of the lithospheric mantle root will bring previously cooler and insulated zones of the lithospheric mantle into direct contact with high asthenospheric temperatures. Partial melting of lithospheric mantle, with its solidus lowered by the addition of volatiles (HS), will follow. The presence of the volcanics therefore supports the hypothesis that convection thinning of thickened lithosphere occurred beneath northern Tibet about 14 Ma ago.

In the 1990s, seismologists identified a zone under northern Tibet that was characterized by unusually slow S-wave velocities (Figure 7.16). This is ascribed to a hot thin lithosphere, which would readily melt due to the shallow depths to which the asthenosphere had risen. This is precisely what the convecting thinning model predicts would happen following the removal of the lithosphere mantle root (Figure 7.15). In summary, we can say that there is a growing body of geological and geophysical evidence that the lithosphere, below at least the northern part of the plateau, has been thinned.

Evidence for lithospheric thinning beneath the southern part of the plateau is more uncertain. Basaltic andesites are older, by 10 to 25 Ma, compared to those in the north. Moreover, seismic surveys indicate unusually *high* S-wave velocities both suggesting a cold and thick lithosphere. It is possible that the lithosphere was thinned earlier beneath southern Tibet but has subsequently cooled and thickened.

  ⬤   Is the interpretation consistent with the viscous sheet model?

  ⬤   Yes. The model predicts progressive thickening from south to north which implies that subsequent thinning will also be initiated in the south before propagating northwards.

By combining the thin viscous sheet model for large-scale continental deformation with convective thinning of the mantle root from the thickened lithosphere, we have a convincing explanation of the geodynamic evolution of Tibet. It is important to emphasize that our approach in this Section has been based largely on theoretical models rather than direct observation. This is because the surface geology of the Tibetan Plateau is comprised largely of Mesozoic and Tertiary sedimentary rocks that have experienced virtually no erosion since the early Neogene. These offer little evidence for the underlying causes of plateau uplift that might be revealed by the structure and metamorphism of deeper crustal levels. In contrast, the Himalaya, like all young mountain ranges, are strongly eroded exposing deep crustal sections for the geologist to evaluate.

7.4.5 Summary of Section 7.4

• The thin viscous sheet model is useful for understanding large-scale deformation of the Tibetan lithosphere.

• Some convergence between India and Eurasia is accommodated by extrusion of the lithosphere eastwards along major strike–slip faults.

• Thickening of the Tibetan lithosphere may lead to the convective removal of a lithospheric mantle root and consequent uplift of the plateau to regain isostatic equilibrium.

• Basaltic andesites erupted in the past 14 Ma in Northern Tibet are probably a thermal response to convective thinning of the lithosphere.

7.5 Tectonics of the Central Himalaya

Whereas a broad plateau area of uplift may behave, on a regional scale, like a thin viscous sheet, uplift of a narrow mountain chain like the Himalaya is much more likely to be controlled by major faults that can be identified in the field. Mountain building in the upper crust is achieved largely by thrust tectonics (Section 2), and the next part of this Section describes the precise geometries of the thrust zones responsible for the elevation of the main arc of the Himalayan chain.

7.5.1 The structure of the Central Himalaya

Although the detailed tectonics of the Himalayan orogen are complex, many of the main lithological units and structures can be traced along strike throughout the central section of the orogen from Zanskar in the west to Everest in the east (Figure 7.2). These are illustrated by a generalized north–south cross-section across the Central Himalaya (Figure 7.19).

> **Question 7.8** Identify the four major fault zones south of the suture (three are thrusts and one is a normal fault). Which Himalayan units do they separate?

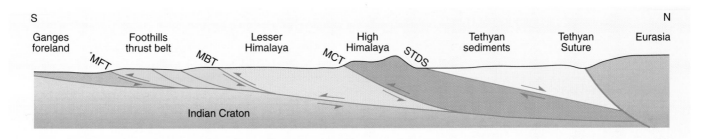

Figure 7.19 Simplified cross-section through the Central Himalaya. MCT = Main Central Thrust; MBT = Main Boundary Thrust; MFT = Main Frontal Thrust; STDS = South Tibetan Detachment System.

Both the Lesser Himalaya and the High Himalaya formations have undergone ductile deformation and metamorphism during the Himalayan orogeny and so comprise the Inner Zone of the orogen. South of the MBT lies the Outer Zone.

The major structures identified on Figure 7.19 can be traced for about 2000 km along strike by numerous traverses up the principal river valleys which drain radially from the Himalaya. Many of these rivers are known to be *antecedent*, i.e. their courses are old and the rivers have cut down like a cheesewire as the mountains rise. This feature is important for it has allowed the Himalaya to erode during crustal shortening to expose the geology that allows us to examine the bulk geometry of thrust zones on a crustal scale.

Although the surface geology of the Central Himalaya is reasonably well established, the geometry of the faults at depth has been the subject of debate. One idea proposed by Peter Molnar is that the principal thrusts form a gross imbricate stack — with the crust repeated by movements on the Main Boundary Thrust and Main Central Thrust. Using these geometries, we can establish a value for the amount of crustal shortening experienced by the northern margin of the Indian continental crust.

> **Question 7.9** (a) By examining Figure 7.20, suggest which came earlier — the MBT or MCT. These thrusts offset the top of basement A–A' and B–B'. (b) Using this information, determine the total offset on these Himalayan thrusts.

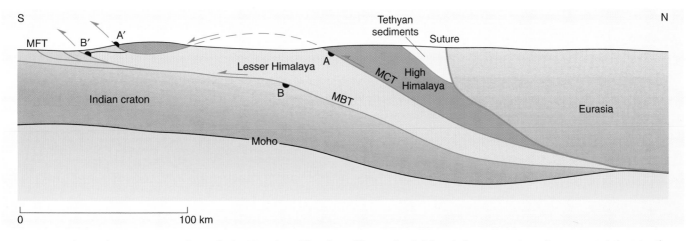

Figure 7.20 Crustal cross-section through the Nepalese Himalaya illustrating Molnar's interpretation of two crustal thrusts, the MCT and MBT, slicing up the Indian continent. The offset of the top of the basement on these thrusts is indicated by A–A' and B–B' respectively.

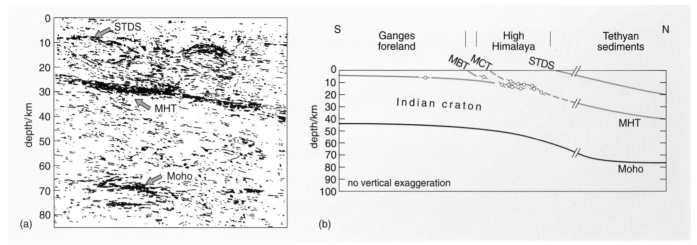

Figure 7.21 (a) Deep seismic reflection profile from INDEPTH. STDS = South Tibetan Detachment System; MHT = Main Himalayan Thrust; MCT = Main Central Thrust; MBT = Main Boundary Thrust. (b) Interpretation of INDEPTH profile from alignment with earthquake foci.

Since paleomagnetic data imply about 450 km shortening across the Himalaya, Molnar's section probably provides an underestimate of shortening.

We can check the proposed geometry of the thrust zone to check its validity by making use of geophysical data that have recently become available. In the mid-1990s, deep seismic reflection data were collected along a north–south traverse in southern Tibet by a joint US–Chinese project (INDEPTH). This imaged three reflection horizons (Figure 7.21a).

The deepest of these is the Moho, located about 70–80 km beneath the surface. A double-thickness crust is confirmed by gravity data.

However, the strongest reflection is located mid-way through the crust and is identified as a major thrust, separating the Tibetan crust above from the underthrust Indian crust. This fault, called the Main Himalayan Thrust (MHT), can be traced southwards and upwards through a zone of earthquake foci with fault-plane solutions indicative of thrusting (Figure 7.21b). Splays of this fault break the surface at the Main Central Thrust (MCT) and the Main Boundary Thrust (MBT).

The INDEPTH survey confirmed Molnar's key predictions for the Central Himalaya. Crustal thickening beneath the Himalaya and southern Tibet is accomplished by underthrusting of thick crustal slices.

One aspect of the Main Himalayan Thrust confirmed by the INDEPTH study is its increasing dip with depth under the Himalaya (Figure 7.21b). This may be related to the thermal structure of the Indian lithosphere, which controls its rigidity and hence its ability to support loads. An important consequence of the Indian lithosphere being depressed at depth will be orogenic collapse in the overriding plate. This is the probable significance of the South Tibetan Detachment System (STDS), an east–west normal fault zone (Figure 7.22) that can be traced along much of the northern edge of the Himalaya (Figure 7.5). We shall return to the significance of the STDS later.

Figure 7.22 The South Tibetan Detachment zone looking eastwards (Zanskar). Pale rocks from the ridge in the foreground are Tethyan sediments. To the right (south) are darker, upfaulted high-grade gneisses from the High Himalayan metasediments.

7.5.2 Metamorphism of the Central Himalaya

We now know that the Himalaya result from rapid crustal thickening during continental collision. From our discussion about the thermal evolution of collision zones, we can predict that the immediate result of overthrusting continental crust on continental crust would be to achieve a saw-tooth geotherm (Section 6.1.2).

> **Question 7.10**   How would the geotherm vary with depth in both the thrust sheet and in the overthrust basement?

In the Himalayan orogen, the rocks exposed between the MBT and the STDS (Figure 7.19) include the metasedimentary formations of the Lesser and High Himalaya. These have been metamorphosed in the following sequence of metamorphic zones increasing in metamorphic grade from south to north: chlorite, biotite, garnet, kyanite, sillimanite (Figure 7.23a).

This is the same sequence as seen in the Barrow zones in the Scottish Highlands, except that staurolite appears with kyanite, so does not identify a distinct zone. However, unlike the Barrow zones, the pressure of the Himalayan zones decreases with increasing metamorphic grade, hence defining an inverted metamorphic gradient.

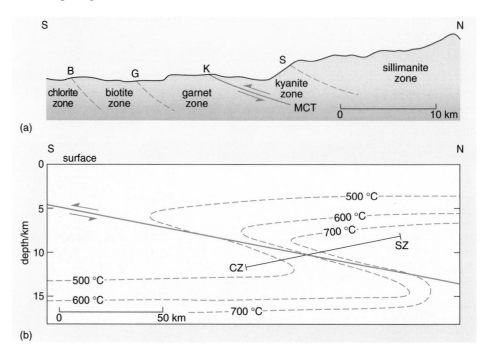

Figure 7.23 (a) Metamorphic section (N–S) across the MCT in the Central Himalaya. Isograds marked as B = biotite; G = garnet; K = kyanite; S = sillimanite. (b) Postulated isotherms resulting from overthrusting caused by movement along the MCT. CZ–SZ indicates section from chlorite zone to sillimanite zone.

One explanation for such a relationship is shown in Figure 7.23b which shows a saw-tooth transient geotherm shortly after thrusting. In this model, the southernmost part of the section in Figure 7.23a lies in the lower slab at less than 500 °C (point CZ), but temperatures rise rapidly in the overlying slab (point SZ) due to the geometry of the saw-tooth geotherm.

Question 7.11   Assuming that the saw-tooth geotherm is the correct explanation for the inverted metamorphic gradient, what are the implications for uplift rates in the area?

The explanation for inverted metamorphism illustrated in Figure 7.23 therefore implies that uplift was so rapid after thrusting along the MCT that mineral assemblages were frozen into a pattern which directly records the saw-tooth transient geotherm. The rate of thermal relaxation is strongly dependent on the thickness of the thrust slices. Since this explanation was first proposed, the theory has been tested by thermal models that are based on appropriate thicknesses of thrust slices and on realistic rates for movement on the MCT and for uplift. Results from this work clearly indicate that an inverted gradient in Himalayan metamorphic rocks will not be preserved because it is not possible to exhume the rocks sufficiently rapidly. Consequently, another explanation is required.

The hanging-wall of the MCT

In order to explain the sequence of Himalayan metamorphic zones, we need to examine the rocks more closely. The rocks in the hanging-wall of the MCT are known as the High Himalaya formations. The P–T fields recorded by these rocks have been studied in some detail using techniques described in Section 6.2.

● Bearing in mind the errors in each *P–T* estimate in Figure 7.24, how would you describe the change in pressure and temperature between the kyanite- and the sillimanite-bearing rocks?

● Although the sillimanite rocks were formed at much lower pressures, it is difficult to say whether the temperatures differed between the sillimanite- and kyanite-bearing assemblages because of the uncertainties in the temperature estimates.

The mineral assemblages of rocks from the sillimanite zone provide additional information on the metamorphic history of the High Himalaya metasediments. The aluminosilicate stable in these gneisses is clearly sillimanite (Figure 7.25a), but garnets from the same rock contain a few inclusions of kyanite (Figure 7.25b).

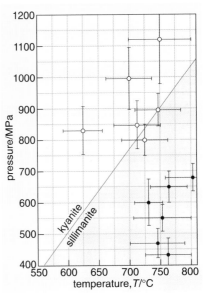

Figure 7.24 Calculated pressures and temperatures for metamorphic rocks from the Langtang Valley in Nepal. Open circles = kyanite zone; filled circles = sillimanite zone.

(a)

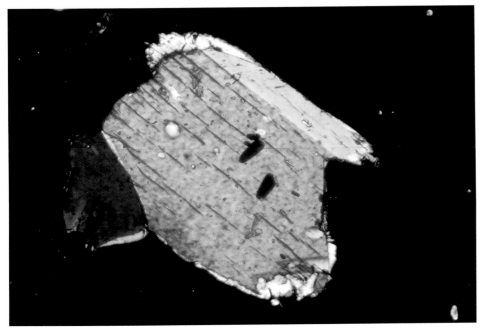

(b)

Figure 7.25 (a) Sillimanite fibres from a sillimanite gneiss from the Central Himalaya seen in plane-polarized light. Width of image = 3.5 mm. (b) Kyanite inclusion in garnet (shown as black) from the same sillimanite gneiss seen under crossed polars. Width of image = 2.2 mm.

● What can you conclude about the timing of growth of the minerals kyanite, garnet and sillimanite?

● Kyanite was the first mineral to grow. Garnet must have grown initially in the stability field of kyanite. Later metamorphism in the sillimanite field recrystallized most of the minerals, but as garnet remained stable the kyanite inclusions within it were preserved.

When this conclusion is considered with the *P–T* data of Figure 7.24, the most likely explanation is that all the rocks were initially metamorphosed in the kyanite zone but those sampled from the sillimanite zone had since undergone a drop of pressure into the sillimanite zone.

So far we have talked rather generally about when these metamorphic events occurred. What we need to consider now is a precise method of dating them (see Box 7.2).

Box 7.2　Dating metamorphic events

You may be familiar with two radiometric methods for dating geological events: dating zircons from igneous rocks, using the decay of uranium (^{238}U, ^{235}U) to lead isotopes (^{206}Pb, ^{207}Pb), and dating whole rock samples of granite using the decay of rubidium (^{87}Rb) to strontium (^{87}Sr) isotopes. Both techniques are particularly useful for dating the crystallization of igneous rocks but less so for unravelling the timing of metamorphic events.

All rocks that go through a metamorphic cycle will heat up on their prograde path and cool down on their retrograde path (Figure 7.26). If the age of mineral growth is required, then it is important to use an isotopic system with a closure temperature that is higher than the peak temperature of metamorphism, bearing in mind that any mineral chronometer dates the time that has passed since the temperature became closed to the daughter isotope. Conversely, if the cooling (retrograde) path is to be dated, then an isotope system should be used with a known closure temperature that is less than that of peak metamorphism.

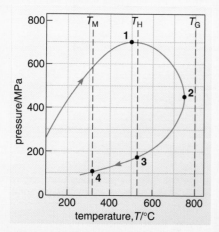

Figure 7.26 Hypothetical *P–T–t* path (arrowed blue loop) for a metamorphic rock. T_M, T_H, T_G are closure temperatures for Ar in muscovite and hornblende and for Nd in garnet respectively. The closure temperature is the temperature below which the element in question cannot diffuse out of the mineral.

Potassium-bearing minerals can be dated using the decay of ^{40}K to ^{39}Ar. The value of K–Ar dating has been greatly increased by the technique called Ar–Ar dating. Samples are irradiated to convert ^{40}K to ^{40}Ar, and then Ar isotopes are measured as $^{40}Ar/^{39}Ar$ ratios. This results in a much better understanding of how the Ar has behaved at different temperatures, and the parallel development of laser systems allows *in situ* analysis of minerals such as hornblende and muscovite. These have closure temperatures for Ar isotopes of about 525 and 320 °C respectively so, provided metamorphism has reached higher temperatures, these minerals are ideal for dating the time at which the rock passes through these temperatures while cooling. For example, in the *P–T–t* loop shown in Figure 7.26, an Ar–Ar hornblende age will record the time elapsed since the rock passed through point 3. The muscovite age will be younger, giving the time elapsed since cooling through point 4.

The development of increasingly sensitive mass spectrometers has allowed the detection of smaller concentrations of U, Th and Pb isotopes. As a result, a wider range of accessory phases can be dated successfully. Moreover, with the development of laser systems, very small grains can be analysed from rock sections, without having to separate them by physical or chemical methods. This means that small grains not only of zircon ($ZrSiO_4$) but also of monazite ($CePO_4$) or titanite ($CaTiO_3$) can be analysed *in situ*. The problem with dating accessory phases though is that these tiny grains do not form part of the metamorphic fabric so their growth usually cannot be related to the deformation or the metamorphism of the rock. If, for example, we know a precise age for a zircon in a metasedimentary rock, how do we interpret that age? Has the zircon been inherited as a detrital grain (in which case its crystallization pre-dates sedimentation), did it grow during an early metamorphic episode, or did it grow more recently during a period of late metamorphism or hydrothermal activity? Under exceptional circumstances, we can observe a textural relationship between metamorphism and the growth of accessory phases. For example, if zircon is seen to be included in a mica which forms the main foliation of the rock, then deformation, and the metamorphism that caused mica growth, must be younger than the age of the zircon. So the *in situ* dating of inclusions can be useful for placing a maximum age on the growth of the host mineral.

In an ideal situation, geologists would date directly the minerals that (i) form the metamorphic fabric and (ii) also provide information on the *P–T* conditions during mineral growth. The result would be a known point on the *P–T–t* path of the rock. The dating of major metamorphic minerals used to obtain pressure and temperature information has become something of a 'Holy Grail' for metamorphic petrologists. With the development of both chemical preparation procedures and mass spectrometer sensitivity, it is now possible to date garnets directly from the low concentrations of rare-earth elements in their structure. **Garnet chronometry** depends on the decay of ^{147}Sm (samarium) to ^{143}Nd (neodymium). By dating garnet cores and rims using Sm–Nd isotopes, and by obtaining *P–T* information on the same minerals, it is possible (i) to date the beginning of garnet growth (from the core) and the end of garnet growth (from the rims) and (ii) to calculate the change in pressure or temperature that the rock experienced during this time. Because Sm and Nd diffuse extremely slowly through the garnet lattice, these ages are not reset for temperatures below 800 °C.

For the *P–T–t* loop shown on Figure 7.26, if we assume the garnet isograd is passed at temperatures above 500 °C then the date of garnet cores could be as old as the time the path passes through point 1. Because garnet is unlikely to grow during cooling, when mineral reactions slow down, the rim of the garnet is likely to record the time elapsed since the rock reached peak metamorphic grade (point 2). For all but the hottest metamorphic events in the granulite facies (where temperatures exceed 800 °C), garnets can provide the timing of prograde metamorphic growth.

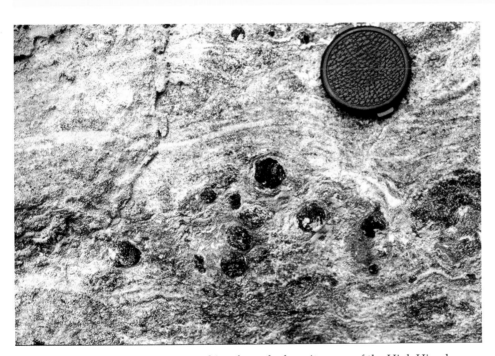

Figure 7.27 Garnet in muscovite schists from the kyanite zone of the High Himalaya metasediments.

Geologists from the Open University have recently undertaken a detailed study of Himalayan garnets from muscovite–garnet schists in the kyanite zone (Figure 7.27), north of the MCT in the Zanskar region of the Central Himalaya (Figure 7.2). Garnet cores were found to have formed at 33.4 ± 0.6 Ma and the youngest garnet rims were formed at 27.5 ± 1.2 Ma indicating that the rocks had experienced the conditions required for garnet growth for a period of at least 6 ± 2 Ma. Even younger garnet rims might be present, but were not sampled.

Question 7.12 Garnets from the kyanite zone from Zanskar are strongly zoned. The variation in Fe/Mg ratio of the garnet relative to co-existing biotite is plotted in Figure 7.28. Using the garnet–biotite thermometer (Figure 6.20), calculate the difference in temperature during the growth of the garnet.

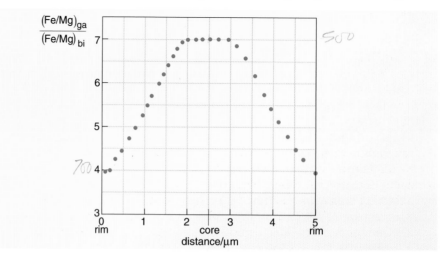

Figure 7.28 Variation in [Fe/Mg] in garnet divided by [Fe/Mg] in co-existing biotite, across a 5 mm garnet crystal.

In addition to zoning, the garnets host many inclusions such as mica, kyanite and feldspar. Detailed work on the pressures and temperatures at which the inclusions were stable indicated that the core inclusions had grown at pressures of 600 ± 50 MPa and temperatures of $560 \pm 20\,°C$ whereas the rim was formed at 1000 ± 50 MPa and $700 \pm 20\,°C$. We can conclude that between 33 and 27 Ma these rocks were being buried and heated, presumably by thrusting (Figure 7.29).

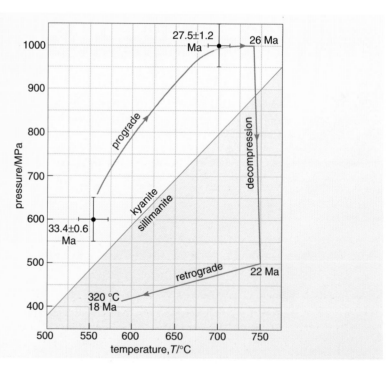

Figure 7.29 Pressure–temperature–time path of a garnet-bearing metasediment from the kyanite zone, Zanskar Himalaya.

Ar–Ar dating of muscovite from the same rocks indicate cooling ages of ~18 Ma. This means the rocks had cooled from their peak of ~700 °C to ~320 °C (the closure temperature of Ar in muscovite) between 27 and 18 Ma.

● How could such a rapid cooling rate be achieved in an orogenic belt?

● The only reasonable way to cool deeply buried rocks through 380 °C in 9 Ma is to exhume the rocks rapidly along a normal fault.

A few kilometres north of the kyanite-grade rocks lies the South Tibetan Detachment System (Figure 7.22) which has exhumed the high-grade rocks to the south so that they became juxtaposed against unmetamorphosed Tethyan sediments to the north (Figure 7.19). Structural studies of the fault in Zanskar indicate a throw of at least 20 km, and radiometric dating of micas that grew in the fault zone indicates that fault movement was initiated around 26 Ma and was still active by 22 Ma. The overall P–T–t loop, shown in Figure 7.29, is obtained by combining the available information. It implies that whereas the kyanite-grade assemblages formed between 33 and 26 Ma, the rocks entered the sillimanite field between 26 and 22 Ma, during decompression.

The footwall of the MCT

Although decompression accounts for sillimanite-grade metamorphism overprinting rocks exhumed from kyanite-grade conditions, it does not account for the inverted metamorphism defined by the chlorite–biotite–garnet zones of the Lesser Himalaya formations from the footwall of the MCT (Figure 7.23). For these zones, there is a real change in temperature of metamorphism from <500 °C in the chlorite zone to ~600 °C in the garnet zone. Although the MCT is often mapped as a single thrust on a regional scale, more detailed mapping has indicated that it forms a ductile shear zone which varies in thickness between 10 and 40 km. The top of this shear zone is sometimes marked by a brittle fault, which often coincides with the kyanite isograd. This raises the possibility that the metamorphic zones originally formed in response to a normal geotherm, with temperatures increasing with depth (Figure 7.30a), but have been since rearranged by post-metamorphic thrusting along the MCT (Figure 7.30b).

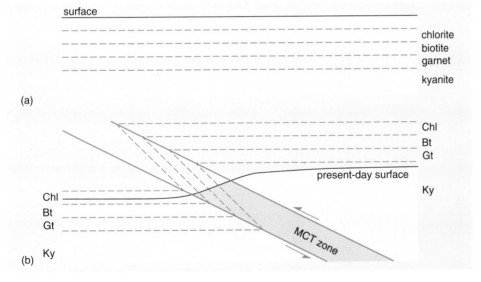

Figure 7.30 The overturning of a normal sequence of metamorphic zones (a) by post-metamorphic thrusting along the MCT (b).

Several geochronological studies of the MCT have suggested that the fault was initially active at about 22 to 20 Ma ago. However, more recent dating of monazites from garnet-zone metasediments (using a technique outlined in Box 7.2) yielded surprisingly young ages of ~6 Ma. Some of these monazites were inclusions within garnets which suggests that within the MCT zone temperatures had been hot enough for garnets to grow as recently as 6 Ma ago. This implies that the MCT is a long-lived structure which has undergone periods of reactivation. This information supports the mechanical (rather than thermal) explanation for inverted metamorphism in the footwall of the MCT as is illustrated in Figure 7.30.

It is now recognized that the initial 'normal' sequence of metamorphic zones formed during thrust tectonics and burial between 33 and 26 Ma ago. Subsequent exhumation along the STDS to the north cooled the rocks in the hanging-wall of the MCT so that the metamorphic zones became 'frozen'. More recent activation of the MCT resulted in an 'S-shaped' pattern for metamorphic zones, overturning the kyanite–garnet–biotite–chlorite sequence within the MCT zone itself (Figure 7.30b). Finally, erosion to the present level of exposure resulted in an apparent metamorphic inversion.

7.5.3 Magmatism in the Central Himalaya

The Main Central Thrust is not only associated with inverted metamorphic zones. A series of very distinctive granites are found to the north of the thrust and south of the STDS (Figure 7.31) which are spread over 1000 km along the strike of the Himalayan chain (Figure 7.5). Only the larger bodies are shown in Figure 7.5, and thousands of smaller pods and sheets are exposed high up in the Himalaya at altitudes of over 3000 m. The intrusions are known as **leucogranites** because of their light colour. Together with quartz and feldspars, they contain muscovite and sometimes biotite or tourmaline (Figure 7.32).

Figure 7.31 A 20 Ma High Himalayan leucogranite (Bhagirathi, 6512 m, Garwhal Himalaya). Contact with dark metasediments is seen towards the top. Cliff height is ~3000 m.

Figure 7.32 A typical High Himalayan leucogranite with crystals of tourmaline (dark) and muscovite (silver).

The High Himalayan leucogranites are volumetrically several orders of magnitude smaller than the Trans-Himalayan plutonic rocks, and were emplaced as a series of lenses and sheet complexes into the high-grade rocks of the High Himalayan metasediments. Chemically, leucogranites are quite distinct from other granites. They differ from subduction-related suites as found in the Andes and the Trans-Himalayan belt in several respects:

- Silica contents of the leucogranites exceed 70%; intermediate compositions such as granodiorites and diorites are not found associated with leucogranites.

- The leucogranites are strongly peraluminous (i.e. molar $Al_2O_3 > CaO + Na_2O + K_2O$) shown in the norm as normative corundum. For the Trans-Himalayan batholith, most compositions are metaluminous (molar $Al_2O_3 < CaO + Na_2O + K_2O$), so that there is normative anorthite but no normative corundum.

- The leucogranites are high in alkali trace elements such as Rb (200–300 ppm) but low in other elements such as Sr and Zr. You can confirm this by comparing LG1, a typical leucogranite, with LP2, a calc-alkaline granite from the Trans-Himalayan batholith (Table 7.1).

- Initial $^{87}Sr/^{86}Sr$ ratios are high in the leucogranites (0.740–0.760) compared to Andean or Trans-Himalayan plutons (0.704–0.708).

The absence of intermediate or basic igneous rocks implies that the leucogranites are not part of a fractionation series with a more basic igneous parent. A peraluminous magma with high alkalis is consistent with partial melting of an alkali-rich aluminous source and the high initial $^{87}Sr/^{86}Sr$ suggests a crustal source rich in Rb. These different strands of evidence suggest that the granite results from the partial melting of an aluminous sediment such as a pelite, which is rich in micas and therefore K, Rb and Al. During partial melting, Sr is strongly partitioned into plagioclase so the low Sr concentrations in the melt suggest residual feldspar.

Such a source for the melts is supported by the observation that the leucogranites commonly contain xenoliths of metasediments (Figure 7.33). In places the metasedimentary rocks are migmatites that appear to have partially

Figure 7.33 Pelitic xenolith in High Himalayan leucogranite.

melted (Figure 7.34). Examination of the minerals in both unmelted and melted examples of the metasediments shows that the mineral muscovite disappears with the appearance of both sillimanite and granitic melt. The melt reaction that is suggested by these observations is given by the equation:

$$\text{muscovite} + \text{quartz} + \text{plagioclase} = \text{melt} + \text{sillimanite} + \text{alkali feldspar} \qquad (7.1)$$

Figure 7.34 A typical migmatite from the sillimanite zone of High Himalaya metasediments.

The melt reaction resulting from muscovite breakdown (Equation 7.1) is an example of **dehydration melting**. This is because muscovite is a hydrous phase (it contains OH^-) and reacts with other minerals to form a melt. When the dehydration melt reaction is crossed, the hydroxyl ions bound in the mica structure are released into the melt allowing a low melt fraction to form, even in the absence of other fluids. In other words, the presence of micas means the system is not entirely dry.

> **Question 7.13** The bulk partition coefficient (D) for Rb during the muscovite melting reaction is 0.30. An unmelted pelitic schist contains 150 ppm Rb. Calculate the proportion of melt required to produce a typical Himalayan leucogranite (Rb = 370 ppm).

Such a low value for the melt fraction responsible for forming the Himalayan leucogranites has important implications for understanding their origin.

Experimental studies on melting Himalayan pelitic schists indicate that the muscovite dehydration melting solidus (Equation 7.1) has a positive slope in P–T space which intersects the solidus for hydrous melting of a pelitic schist at pressures of ~250 MPa (Figure 7.35).

> **Question 7.14** From the P–T data for sillimanite-grade rocks in the Central Himalaya (Figure 7.24), under what conditions would a melt form in these rocks?

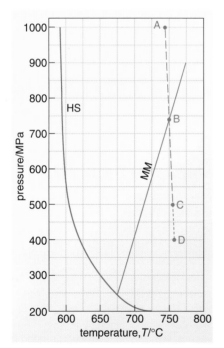

Figure 7.35 The hydrous (wet) solidus for melting of pelitic sediments in the presence of water (HS) and the solidus for the muscovite partial melting reaction in the absence of water (MM). Dashed line A–D indicates possible exhumation path leading to melting.

Early studies of the leucogranites proposed that melting had been induced in the hanging-wall of the MCT by fluids infiltrating from the thrust zone into the hot rocks above.

● Why should fluids infiltrating hot rocks induce melting?

● From Figure 7.35, granite melts can form at lower temperatures in the presence of hydrous fluids. Therefore, a dry rock containing quartz, plagioclase and muscovite that is at a temperature above the hydrous solidus will melt in the presence of an infiltrating fluid.

But this hypothesis failed to account for the fact that the granites had formed, not immediately above the thrust zone, where fluids would be most abundant and rocks would be hottest, but several kilometres further up the section, adjacent to the STDS (Figure 7.5). Indeed we now know that the granites have been emplaced near the roof of a tectonic wedge bound below by the MCT and above by the STDS (Figure 7.36).

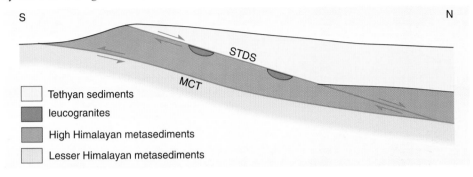

Figure 7.36 Tectonic setting of Himalayan leucogranites. The wedge is bounded by the South Tibetan Detachment System (STDS) and the Main Central Thrust (MCT).

The wet melting hypothesis also failed to account for the low melt fraction calculated from the trace-element concentrations in the granites and their source rocks (Question 7.13). During dehydration melting, the size of the melt fraction depends largely on the proportion of muscovite in the source but for typical modal proportions of muscovite found in unmelted Himalayan pelites, melt fractions of 0.08 to 0.15 would be expected. Hydrous melting allows a much higher melt fraction from rocks of this composition, in excess of 0.4. So we can account for the trace-element chemistry of the granite by dehydration melting, but not by wet melting. The question that now arises is what caused these rocks to cross the dehydration melting reaction in the first place?

Although dating metamorphic processes is difficult, dating igneous bodies is relatively simple. Many of the Himalayan leucogranites have now been dated, mostly by zircon and monazite dating, and the great majority of these ages are Neogene, in the range 24 to 19 Ma.

> **Question 7.15** By comparing the P–T–t loop for Himalayan metapelitic sediments from the hanging-wall of the MCT (Figure 7.29) with the phase diagram for dehydration melting (Figure 7.35), can you propose an origin for crustal melts of this age?

A possible exhumation path is plotted in Figure 7.35. From A to B, the rock remains in a solid state. From B to C, partial melting may form migmatites and granite melts under sillimanite-grade conditions. At some stage during exhumation, the melt will segregate from its source and ascend through the crust (C–D). The melt will crystallize once it reaches the STDS (Figure 7.36) where it will be chilled by the cold Tethyan sediments in the hanging-wall.

Although decompression melting has been recognized in the mantle beneath ocean ridges, this is the first time it has been proposed for crustal rocks. It is possible only because the dehydration melting curve has a positive slope in P–T space (Figure 7.35). For wet melting, decreasing the pressure will only drive a melt towards or across the solidus, causing crystallization. Thus the High Himalayan leucogranites, although not large volumetrically, have provided some important clues to the consequences of crustal thickening and exhumation. They have highlighted the role of active thrusts and detachment zones and have established a melting mechanism which does not require heating of the source rocks to generate a melt. The Himalayan leucogranites are in fact the type example of granite formation through crustal melting in response to continental collision.

7.5.4 Summary of Section 7.5

- Deformation in the Central Himalaya is controlled by major thrust zones which separate imbricated crustal-scale thrust slices.

- Both the distribution of metamorphic zones and the timing of melt formation in the Himalaya can be understood from the tectonic evolution of the orogen.

- In the hanging-wall of the MCT, the apparent inversion of a sillimanite zone over a kyanite zone results from an overprinting of a low pressure assemblage on a high pressure assemblage.

- Precise garnet dating indicates that in the Central Himalaya prograde heating up above the garnet–isograd occurred between 33 and 26 Ma followed by decompression from the kyanite to sillimanite field between 26 and 22 Ma.

- In the footwall of the MCT, the inverted metamorphic zones result from the overturning of a normal sequence of isograds by post-metamorphic movement on the MCT zone.

- Abundant leucogranites emplaced south of the STDS between 24 and 19 Ma result from melting of metapelitic sediments.

- Crustal melting results from dehydration melting of muscovite in the source rocks.

- The cause of melting is the rapid drop in pressure experienced by the rocks as they were exhumed in the footwall of a major detachment, the STDS.

7.6 Tectonics of the Western Himalaya

Visitors to northern Pakistan could be greatly misled if they were to assume that topographic elevation reflected the geology as simply as has been established in Nepal and southern Tibet. The only rocks of the Indian continent which are associated with substantial elevation are those in the core of the Nanga Parbat syntaxis. This odd promontory of Indian basement rocks shown between Kohistan and Ladakh in Figure 7.5 is the north-west termination of the Himalayan range. The peak of Nanga Parbat (8125 m) is some 4 km higher than the equivalent geology to the south-west (Figure 7.37) and this region is the most active of the entire Himalayan orogen.

Figure 7.37 The southern face of Nanga Parbat (8125 m).

7.6.1   The structure of the Western Himalaya

We can examine the structure of the Western Himalaya on a north–south section which runs from the suture zone (here the Main Mantle Thrust) to the foreland on the Indian plains (Figure 7.38).

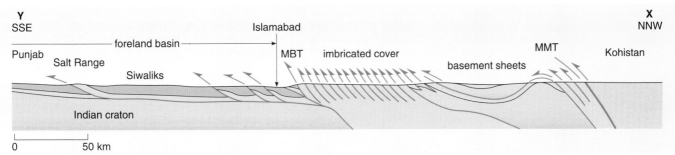

The major difference between the Western and Central Himalaya sections is that, in Pakistan, the thrust sheets are thinner and collectively much more complex. In the north, the thrusts carry thin slices of basement rocks — structures equivalent to the metasedimentary formations of the High Himalaya. To the south lie numerous repetitions of the Phanerozoic cover sediments of the Indian continent. South of the MBT lies the foreland basin filled with alluvial sediments called the Siwaliks, eroded from the rising mountains to the north. The name is taken from a range of hills north of Delhi. But in Pakistan, thrusting has migrated far out into the foreland basin to uplift the Salt Range. From regional geophysical data, we know that basement is not involved in these southernmost structures. This suggests that there is a thrust detachment of basement from cover. If true, Molnar's simple model of a few crustal-scale thrusts is not applicable along the Pakistan sector of the mountain belt. The implications of this contrast in structural style are profound.

Detailed structural mapping through northern Pakistan implies about 500 km N–S shortening within the upper crustal rocks south of the MMT over a distance of 250 km, i.e. shortening from 750 to 250 km. If this value applied to the entire crust (assuming an original thickness of 30 km), the present-day thickness should be 90 km. Yet despite this, the topographic elevation of the thrust belt averages about 2000 m — about half that of the Central Himalaya. Clearly, the whole thickness of the Indian continent cannot be shortened by 500 km in the Pakistan sector, yet we must achieve a balance between upper and lower crust. What might be the solution to this enigma?

To achieve a balance between upper and lower crustal shortening, we might predict that the northern margin of the Indian continent extends northwards beneath the Kohistan terrane (Figure 7.39). In this way, although the upper crust is greatly thickened, the overall crustal thickness south of the MMT is not

Figure 7.38 Simplified cross-section through the Himalayan thrust belt in northern Pakistan inferred from surface geology (see Figure 7.5 for location).

Figure 7.39 Speculative crustal scale cross-section through northern Pakistan. This shows shortening of the Indian upper crust south of the thickened Indian lower crust beneath Kohistan and the Karakorum.

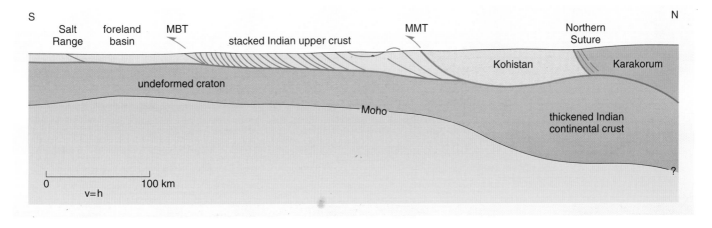

enormously thick. Hence, the topography here is not spectacular. The lower crust thickens up further north — explaining the greater crustal thickness and surface elevation of the Kohistan and Karakorum mountains.

7.6.2 Foreland basin evolution and its disruption

So far, we have examined the evolution of the Himalaya on a large scale and have gained some insight into crustal-scale thrusting processes. We can now investigate how this deformation controls and modifies geological processes operating at the Earth's surface.

● What will happen to the crust when loaded by thrust sheets?

● The result will be subsidence. The loaded plate will flex, generating a sedimentary basin ahead of the load.

South of the Himalaya lie the plains of the Ganges and the Punjab foreland basin. These regions have subsided following crustal shortening in the adjacent mountains and are underlain by alluvial sediments, reaching thicknesses as great as 7 km. Such basins are repositories for some of the detritus eroded from the growing mountains: most resides in the Indus and Ganges deltas. To the south of the Himalayan foothills, the Moho gently dips southward due to flexural loading — rather like a springboard (Figure 7.39). The foreland basin is over 250 km wide suggesting that the Indian continental lithosphere behaves with great rigidity. The Indian continent is, for the most part, old shield material and hence is cold and strong. This ability to support loads generates the wide foreland basin.

Activity 7.3

Now try Activity 7.3 which examines deformation within the foreland basin. You should take about one hour to do this Activity.

The conclusion from this Activity is that thrusting in the foreland basin has migrated extremely rapidly, almost three times faster than the actual shortening rate. The geology of the Salt Range holds the key to understanding these contrasting rates. At the base of the cover sequence is a vast thickness of late Precambrian–Early Cambrian evaporites. As we have seen from the Chartreuse massif in the Alps (Section 2.2), evaporites are weaker than most other sedimentary units and hence are readily activated as thrust detachments during compressional tectonic episodes. It seems likely that, once thrusts have cut upwards into these evaporites, they were able to migrate rapidly out into the foreland basin. This process has greatly influenced the Quaternary geology of the region, resulting in the young uplift of a chain of hills and in the disruption of drainage patterns within the basin.

Before leaving the foreland basin, we can compare the short time-averaged thrusting rate south of Islamabad — about $15 \, \text{km Ma}^{-1}$ — with the gross rate of convergence across the Himalaya. We know from structural sections that a total of $c.\ 500 \, \text{km}$ N–S shortening of the Indian continent has occurred since collision about 50 Ma ago. This implies a time-averaged rate of thrusting of about $10 \, \text{km Ma}^{-1}$, a figure roughly comparable with that obtained for the past 2 Ma in the foreland basin. It seems that in northern Pakistan at least, the present tectonic activity forms a representative time slice for the long-term evolution of the Himalaya.

7.6.3 The exhumation of Nanga Parbat

The virtue of studying very young mountain ranges is that the exhumation history can be studied quantitatively and in some detail.

⬤ What techniques might be appropriate to such studies of exhumation?

⬤ Two techniques are relevant; fission track dating and Ar–Ar dating.

Box 7.3 Dating the cooling path of metamorphism

Fission track ages define the time that a particular mineral experienced its specific closure temperature. These temperatures vary from mineral to mineral. Particularly important, because they are such common minerals, are zircon and apatite, which have closure temperatures of about 200 °C and 125 °C respectively. Higher temperature data can be obtained using radiogenic dating — particularly Ar isotope data applied to the minerals hornblende and muscovite. These have closure temperatures of 525 and 320 °C respectively.

The use of Ar isotope data has a different physical significance to a fission track closure temperature, though it can be used as a fossil thermometer in the same way. Provided a particular rock contains all four minerals (zircon, apatite, muscovite and hornblende) we can determine four different ages that mark the time the rock was exhumed through four distinct temperatures (525, 320, 200 and 125 °C). If our ideal rock can be dated using the four useful minerals (hornblende and muscovite by Ar isotopes, zircon and apatite by fission tracks), we can determine the time at which the rock was at the depths corresponding to the four closure temperatures (Figure 7.40). In this example, the ages are 18 Ma, 12 Ma, 9 Ma and 7 Ma for hornblende, muscovite, zircon and apatite respectively. These ages, when plotted against the relevant closure temperatures, form a near linear array that suggests the rock reached the surface ~ 3 Ma ago. This equates to a cooling rate of 525 °C in 15 Ma, or an average cooling rate of 35 °C Ma^{-1}. If we then assume a geothermal gradient that remains constant with time (say 30 °C km^{-1}) we can establish an exhumation rate of about 1.2 km Ma^{-1}, or about 1.2 mm yr^{-1}, for the uplift of rocks towards the Earth's surface.

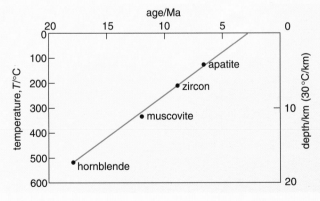

Figure 7.40   Diagrammatic representation of how exhumation rates can be determined, using Ar and fission track ages, assuming a constant geothermal gradient.

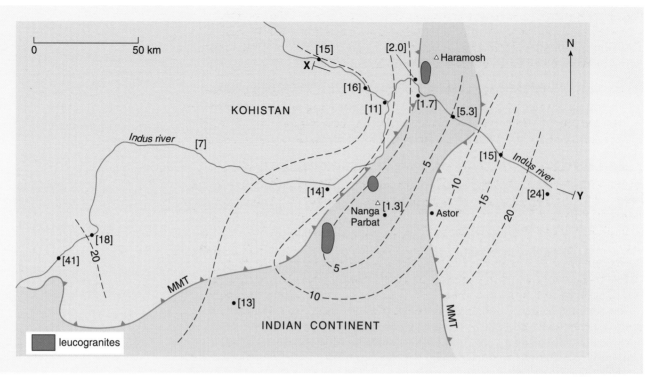

Figure 7.41 Highly simplified map of the Nanga Parbat area showing the loop in the trace of the Main Mantle Thrust. Also plotted are fission track ages of zircon. Ages are shown in square brackets with contour intervals set at 5 Ma. X–Y is the profile line for Figure 7.42.

The most startling exhumation rates have come from the north-western Himalaya of Pakistan where the distribution of zircon fission track ages (Figure 7.41) shows some intriguing features. Although there are relatively few sample locations for such a wide area, the very youngest ages run down the heart of the Nanga Parbat syntaxis. The age of 1.3 Ma for zircon sampled from an outcrop on the slopes of Nanga Parbat comes from an altitude of over 4000 m suggesting very fast exhumation indeed. It is tempting to relate this rapid exhumation rate to the enormous height of Nanga Parbat (8125 m) which stands about 4 km higher than most of the ground to the south and west (Figure 7.37).

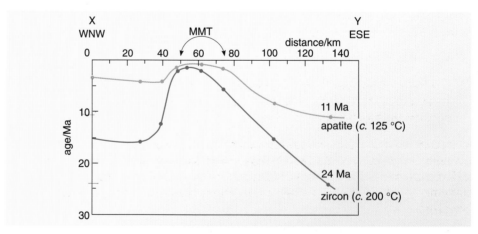

Figure 7.42 Fission track profile across the Nanga Parbat syntaxis (see Figure 7.41 for location). The closure temperature for zircon (c. 250 °C) is higher than that for apatite (c. 125 °C) so zircon ages are older than apatite at each point on the traverse.

Fortunately, there is a continuous section across the Nanga Parbat syntaxis provided by the Indus river and its tributaries which run in a WNW–ESE direction. Apatite and zircon data from northern Pakistan can be plotted on a graph of W–E distance against age (Figure 7.42).

> **Question 7.16** We can use the fission track profiles to determine some useful tectonic information. What is the rate of cooling at the eastern end of the section? Where is the site of the maximum cooling rate? Do you think the exhumation rate is faster on the east or the west side of the syntaxis?

When combined with Ar isotope dating, we find that the Nanga Parbat syntaxis has cooled by more than 525 °C in the past 10 Ma and that this cooling has accelerated. To convert this to an exhumation rate, we must make assumptions regarding the geothermal gradient and erosion. Assuming a normal continental geotherm, the best estimate of exhumation is 5 to 7 mm yr^{-1} (5 to 7 km Ma^{-1}) averaged over the past 3 Ma. Since rates of 2–3 mm yr^{-1} typify the exhumation of most of the Central Himalaya, this value represents the fastest rate recognized in the Himalaya. Small areas adjacent to active faults in New Zealand are faster (up to 40 mm yr^{-1}), but for a continuous exhumation from over 20 km depth in the crust to the Earth's surface the Nanga Parbat syntaxis takes some beating.

Activity 7.4

This Activity examines the structures that are responsible for the exhumation of the western margin of the Nanga Parbat syntaxis. You should take about one hour to do this Activity.

In completing this Activity, you should have discovered that the western margin of the syntaxis is a major thrust fault — the Liachar Thrust — carrying Indian basement gneisses up to the NW, eventually onto Quaternary river gravels. Since the video was made, several small muscovite–tourmaline leucogranites have been discovered intruding the metasediments of the syntaxis close to its western margin (Figure 7.41). Monazite dating from the intrusions indicates very young ages of between 1 and 9 Ma, making them some of the youngest exposed granites on Earth and certainly much younger than the leucogranites of the Central Himalaya (~ 20 Ma). Their high Sr isotope ratios ($^{87}Sr/^{86}Sr = 0.85$) clearly indicate a crustal source.

- What could be the cause of the crustal melting that formed these granites?

- Given the position of their emplacement into the most rapidly exhumed segments of the syntaxis and their very young ages, an origin by decompression melting seems likely.

So it seems that the leucogranites from Nanga Parbat and the older 20 Ma leucogranites from the Central Himalaya were both emplaced during a period of decompression. However, the nature of the faults and the timing of movement on the faults responsible for decompression are quite distinct in the two areas.

The story of uplift of the Nanga Parbat massif is an excellent illustration of the links between processes operating deep in the crust — generating granites and metamorphism — with sedimentation at the Earth's surface. We can examine

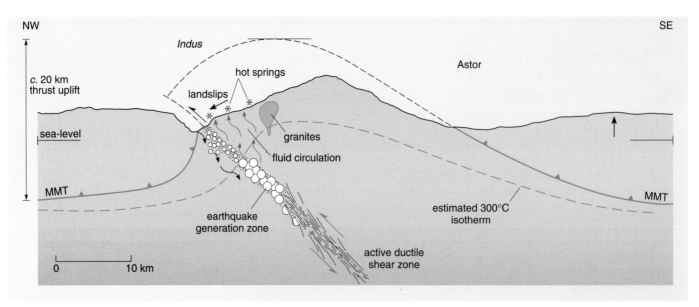

Figure 7.43 Speculative cross-section through the Nanga Parbat syntaxis. The circles along the Liachar Thrust zone represent earthquakes. Faulting is accompanied by fluid circulation along the fault zone.

aspects of the uplift of Nanga Parbat using a cross-section (Figure 7.43). It shows the asymmetric uplift along the Liachar Thrust and illustrates how this thrust changes character from a seismic, brittle structure near the surface to an aseismic, ductile shear zone at depth. The total vertical uplift is about 20 km. Note that the MMT has been folded into a syncline in the footwall to the Liachar Thrust. This is diagnostic of folding related to a thrust tip. The cross-section shows that the Liachar Thrust itself has an offset of only about 5 km so that much of the uplift has been generated by folding. The simplest interpretation is that the Nanga Parbat syntaxis is behaving as a fault-tip fold (Section 2.2.3) perhaps to a large, crustal-scale thrust.

It is likely that this uplift has deformed the thermal structure beneath the mountain, in a similar fashion to the generation of saw-tooth geotherms (Figure 6.7). In ground which displays dramatic variations of topography, the near-surface thermal structure is likely to be extremely complex — and this rather undermines the simple assumption of a constant geothermal gradient through time that we needed to interpret the fission track data. An additional problem for interpreting exhumation rates is the fluid circulation in the hanging-wall of the thrust — a process that will be enhanced by earthquake activity (Figure 7.43). We see the output as hot springs at the surface. Such fluids will aid the convection of heat and so disturb the geotherm. Nonetheless, more detailed modelling of exhumation rates in the region has confirmed that the Nanga Parbat syntaxis is being exhumed much more rapidly than the Central Himalaya.

7.6.4 Summary of Section 7.6

- Deformation in the Western Himalaya is characterized by thinner upper crustal slices, compared to the Central Himalaya, resulting in more modest topography.

- South of the Western Himalaya a 250 km foreland basin results from flexure of the lithosphere loaded by thrust sheets.

- Thrusting within the Siwalik sediments in the foreland basin indicates that deformation has migrated rapidly southwards due to thrust detachments exploiting weak evaporites.

- By combining fission track and Ar isotope data, an exhumation rate of 5–7 mm yr^{-1}, has been obtained from the Nanga Parbat syntaxis, the fastest rates being found along its western margin.

- Exhumation and uplift result from top to the NW movement along the Liachar Thrust which places Precambrian gneisses on top of Quaternary gravels.

- Rapid exhumation along the Liachar Thrust has led to decompression melting of the basement gneisses.

- The MMT forms a syncline in the footwall of the Liachar Thrust, the southern limb of which has been broken by the Liachar Thrust.

7.7   The regional structure of the Himalaya

The overall form of the Himalayan mountains is a narrow arc measuring about 2500 km along strike (Figure 7.1). We can now broaden the discussion to consider the regional context of this arc, and in particular why it is terminated on its western margin by the Nanga Parbat syntaxis.

Because the Himalaya represents a former plate boundary, and continues to be a zone of intense deformation, we would expect that the Himalayan arc might link into active plate margins at each extremity. If you examine the Sunda arc south of the Java trench in the eastern Indian Ocean on the *Geological Map of the World*, you will see this is an east–west striking subduction zone. This plate margin can be traced westwards (Figure 7.44) where its strike curves north-westwards before reaching the Burmese coast. Along this segment, convergence is oblique and the resulting plate movements can be partitioned into two components, dip–slip and strike–slip. The margin runs onshore in Burma where it becomes a north–south system of dextral strike–slip faults (e.g. Kaladan Fault, Figure 7.44). The location of this fault is clearly visible on a topographic map as a curvilinear mountain chain (Figure 7.1). It is this continental strike–slip fault

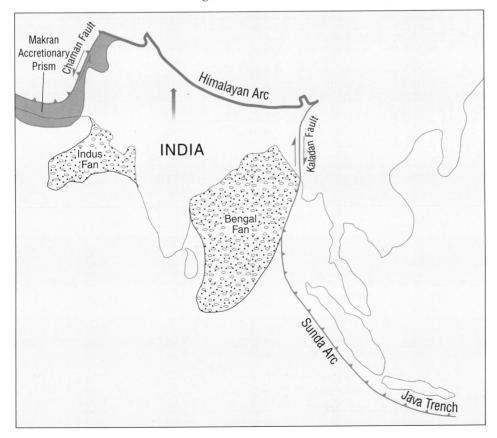

Figure 7.44 The regional tectonic framework of the Himalayan arc.

that terminates the eastern extremity of the Himalayan arc. It also bounds the eastern margin of the Bengal Fan (Figure 7.44), the result of submarine deposition of detritus eroded from the uplifted Himalaya by the Ganges and Brahmaputra rivers.

To the west of the Himalayan arc, regional tectonics are complicated by the Makran accretionary prism in Iran and eastern Afghanistan (Figure 7.44). An accretionary prism is a predictable consequence of active subduction (see Figure 1.1) and the apparent absence of a thick sedimentary prism south of the Tethyan Suture in the Himalaya has promoted some geologists to speculate that post-collision strike–slip faulting has displaced much of the arc eastwards. The north-west margin of the Makran prism is bounded by the Chaman Fault, a sinistral strike–slip fault that effectively terminates the western end of the Himalayan arc. In many respects the Chaman Fault is the western equivalent of the Kaladan Fault in Burma.

The form of the mountain ranges that connect these two continental strike–slip faults is clearly curved (Figure 7.44), which may remind you of a typical volcanic arc. For example, using the *Geological Map of the World*, compare the curvature of the Himalaya with that of the Java trench. In both cases, the arc is convex towards the underthrust side of subduction (i.e. to the south). The distinct curvature of the Himalaya probably reflects the form of the Tethyan arc prior to collision. What is important here is that the curvature of arcs at subduction zones imposes regional stresses on the lithosphere, both sides of the suture zone.

Movement directions within the MMT in the Western Himalaya have established that thrusting is dominantly towards the SSE (Activity 7.1), and a regional study of stretching lineations indicates that thrusting directions along the strike of the Himalaya pick out a radial pattern. This picture is mimicked by fault-plane solutions determined from earthquakes along the front of the Himalaya (Figure 7.45).

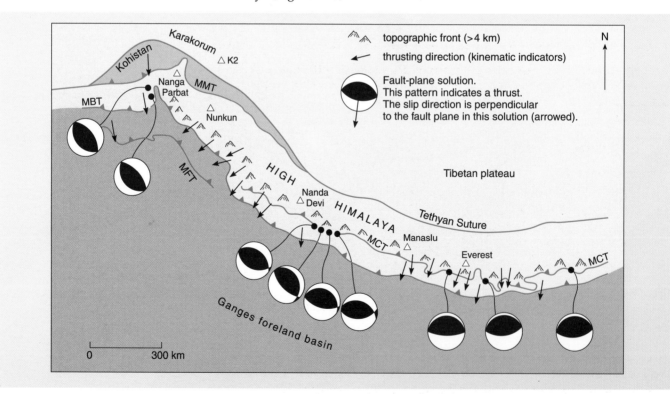

Figure 7.45 Movement directions on thrusts around the Himalayan arc, using active faults (fault-plane solutions) and ancient shear zones (movement axes marked by arrows). Note that these directions (active and ancient) are parallel for each segment of the arc — except to the NW (northern Pakistan). MMT = Main Mantle Thrust; MCT = Main Central Thrust; MBT = Main Boundary Thrust; MFT = Main Frontal Thrust.

- Can these movement directions be related directly to the convergence of rigid plates?

- No. In order to achieve a radial pattern of movement directions, one or both of the plates must deform.

This leads us back to the origin of the odd loop in the outcrop trace of the MMT. Note on Figure 7.5 that there is a further loop of the MBT called the Hazara syntaxis just north of Islamabad. In both cases, rocks are brought up in the core of these structures from lower levels. At Nanga Parbat the Indian continental crust that was buried by movements on the MMT beneath Kohistan is exhumed, while, at Hazara, sediments from below the MBT are exposed.

Question 7.17   Using the information given above, what is the regional structure of the Nanga Parbat and Hazara syntaxes?

We can conclude that the radial thrusting of the main Himalayan chain terminates at two major fold structures. They both imply shortening parallel to the strike of the arc.

In order to understand the causes of this shortening, we need to consider the kinematics of plate movement along the Himalayan arc. Paleomagnetic and ocean-floor magnetic anomaly data indicate that the direction of convergence between India and Eurasia is north–south. This means that, along most of the arc, there is an angle between the direction of convergence and the direction of thrust movement (angle 'θ' in Figure 7.46). Only at one location, which happens to be close to the longitude of Everest, are these two directions parallel. At all other locations, convergence is slightly oblique.

- When convergence is oblique, what are the components into which plate movements can be partitioned?

- From our discussion of the Sunda arc, dip–slip and strike–slip components.

The magnitude of the stress acting along the strike–slip component (i.e. shear stress) is directly related to angle θ (Figure 7.46). West of Everest, this angle increases and so does the shear stress on the lithosphere.

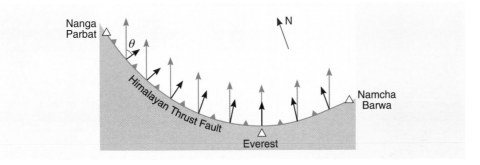

Figure 7.46   The geometry of the Himalayan collision. The angle between direction of plate convergence (purple long arrows) and the direction of movement along the thrusts (black short arrows) is given by 'θ'.

The consequences of this changing stress field along the arc are two-fold. First, it will cause extension north of the arc, in Southern Tibet, and secondly it will cause compressional stress within the arc which progressively increases in intensity towards the west. There is some evidence for current extension in Southern Tibet in the form of north–south graben and dyke swarms, both of which post-date the initial collision (Figure 7.47). More importantly for this discussion, the antiforms of the Nanga Parbat and Hazara syntaxes are believed by some geologists to reflect arc-parallel shortening at the westward termination of the arc.

Figure 7.47 Fault-scarp bounding north–south graben from southern Tibet.

Subduction beneath a curved margin should result in shortening not only in the west but at both extremities of the Himalayan arc because θ increases to the east of Everest as well as to the west (Figure 7.46). Recent studies in south-east Tibet have discovered an antiformal syntaxis near Namcha Barwa on the eastern margin of the Himalayan arc (Figures 7.2, 7.48). Although not as well studied as the Nanga Parbat syntaxis, preliminary results suggest remarkable similarities. These include an antiformal structure, and rapid, recent exhumation of the basement.

An origin for either syntaxis based on regional kinematics is far from being universally accepted. Alternative theories for the origin of the Nanga Parbat syntaxis include the pre-collision structure of the Mesozoic basin within the Himalayan crust and the geometry of the initial impact, with the Western Himalaya bearing the brunt of the collision.

Figure 7.48 An aerial view over Namcha Barwa (7756 m) across the Tsangpo Valley and eastern Tibet.

One of the more unusual theories is that the erosive power of the Indus river, which skirts around the Nanga Parbat syntaxis (Figure 7.41), could drive a cycle of crustal weakening and uplift. The Indus is a powerful river fed by a snow-covered catchment area of over 100 000 km² from the Tibetan Plateau in the spring. It has been argued that erosion by the Indus weakens the crust by cutting a groove through its upper surface while the crust is being uplifted.

Rapid erosion at the surface also causes isostatic compensation at the base of the crust by rising mantle material. This may melt, thus further weakening the crust leading to buckling and the formation of a syntaxis. All of these factors may well have contributed to the formation of the syntaxis.

7.7.1 Summary of Section 7.7

- The Himalayan arc is terminated by regional strike–slip faults that link it to subduction systems in Iran and South-East Asia.

- Movement directions along the Himalaya are radial, requiring deformation of the plates.

- Arc-parallel shortening at the extremities of the Himalaya is a result of oblique convergence.

- The Himalayan extremities are marked by two antiformal syntaxes that can be explained by arc-parallel shortening.

Objectives for Section 7

Now that you have completed this Section, you should be able to:

7.1 Understand the meaning of all the terms printed in **bold**.

7.2 Critically discuss the evidence for the sites of sutures in the Himalayan mountain belt.

7.3 Relate the timing and composition of Himalayan magmatism to the evolving tectonic framework of the Himalaya and southern Tibet.

7.4 Compare and contrast thrust tectonics and the viscous sheet model as mechanisms for crustal thickening and discuss their thermal implications.

7.5 Discuss the relationship between crustal shortening, extrusion and uplift of the Tibetan Plateau.

7.6 Use shear sense and other kinematic indicators to determine the movement direction on thrusts and shear zones, and relate these to plate motions.

7.7 Explain the relationships between metamorphism and tectonics in the Himalaya.

7.8 Describe the geochronological techniques that underpin our understanding of the thermal evolution of the orogen.

7.9 Interpret the origin of Himalayan crustal melts through a consideration of their chronology and geochemistry and a knowledge of the tectonic framework in which they form.

7.10 Relate the development, filling and deformation of foreland basins to the tectonic evolution of the Himalaya.

7.11 Explain how Ar-isotope and fission track data can be used to determine the cooling and exhumation history of the Nanga Parbat syntaxis.

7.12 Compare and contrast the tectonic evolution of the Central and Western Himalaya.

7.13 Describe the geometry of the Himalayan orogen and discuss its implications for regional tectonics.

8 Concluding remarks

This Block has examined the process of mountain building on a range of length scales from thin sections to entire mountain ranges. It has drawn on a wide range of techniques for interpreting the mechanical and thermal histories of deformed rocks. It has also illustrated orogenic processes using several global examples, but the Block began and ended with the Himalaya and Tibet. You may have wondered how good a guide is this orogenic belt for interpreting more ancient mountain belts. In the case of orogenic belts, is the present really the key to the past?

There is no doubt that the Himalaya and Tibet represent the most complete, as well as the most recent, record of continent–continent collision on Earth. But within this region two rather different stories have emerged. The formation of the arcuate belt of the Himalayan mountains is readily understood from the perspective of plate tectonics. The theory of plate tectonics, that regards the Earth's surface as a mosaic of rigid plates, predicts that the release of the Earth's energy, whether in the form of earthquakes, volcanic eruptions or rock deformation, will be largely concentrated in narrow belts along the margins of the plates. A glance at a topographic map of the Earth will confirm that many of the Earth's great mountain ranges, like the Andes, the Rockies or the Atlas, conform to this view. And other ranges that apparently lie inboard of continental margins, like the Alps, the Urals and of course the Himalaya, are the sites of former plate margins that have evolved into collision zones. For all such linear belts, a similar story of crustal thickening largely by thrust tectonics can be told.

The Tibetan Plateau though does not fit well with this world view. From studying this impressive feature we learn that within continental lithosphere, stresses sufficient to greatly thicken the lithosphere can be propagated over distances of thousands of kilometres within the continents themselves. This observation suggests that the continental lithosphere can behave more as a viscous sheet than as a rigid plate. Such broad belts of deformation are not predicted by plate tectonics but requires an entirely fresh mind set guided more by the principles of fluid mechanics than by conventional structural geology. Geologists have made analogies with other plateaux on the Earth's surface, for example the Altiplano eastwards of the central Andes, and the Colorado Plateau in the western United States, but none have the vast dimensions of Tibet, nor indeed have formed so obviously from the collision between two continents. So, is the Tibetan Plateau unique in Earth's history?

This is a question that has kept geologists arguing well into the night on many field trips. It is clear that there are no obvious examples in the Phanerozoic record. As for the Precambrian, the record is so fragmented and reworked by late orogenies that it is impossible to say with any certainty. There is not a single Precambrian orogenic belt where geologists can agree on the original dimensions of the mountain belt, the geometry of collision or even, in many cases, whether there was a collision at all. Given the complexities of events that formed the Tibetan Plateau and the Himalaya, many of which we have only come to understand because we can now date them with a precision of less than a million years, this is scarcely surprising. However, it is fair to say that the uplift of a plateau as large and as high as Tibet is a most unusual event. Clearly, it requires a head-on collision between continents, but equally it requires that the convergent forces are not partitioned onto other plate boundaries. To raise Tibet, the driving force behind the initial convergence must persist over tens of millions of years.

Answers and comments to Questions

Question 1.1 The three phases are:

(i) From 70 to 52 Ma, India was drifting northward at an average rate of about 150 mm yr⁻¹.

(ii) From 52–36 Ma, the motion slowed down and became erratic with changing direction.

(iii) From 36 Ma to the present, India has settled into a northward direction of convergence at a rate of a little less than 50 mm yr⁻¹.

This information suggests that collision occurred between 52 and 36 Ma when the erratic movement and deceleration of India are consistent with a collision.

Question 1.2 The answer depends on the timing of collision and the rate of relative convergence after this time. If an average rate of 50 mm yr⁻¹ (equivalent to 50 km Ma⁻¹) is assumed, and collision is taken at 40 Ma, this suggests 2000 km of convergence. However, if collision was at 50 Ma, then 2500 km of convergence will have occurred. At the time of writing, many geologists consider that 2400 km is probably a realistic value.

Question 2.1 In every case, the stratigraphy shows that older units are present in the hanging-wall of the fault when compared to the footwall. This relationship demonstrates a reverse sense of movement and is characteristic of thrust faults.

Question 2.2 The weakest horizons will host the thrust flats and the best candidates are the thick shale unit at the base of the Cretaceous and the evaporites at the base of the Triassic. These two horizons do indeed locate the thrust flats.

Question 2.3 Figure A2.1 shows the annotated features.

Question 2.4 Figure A2.2 shows the annotated features.

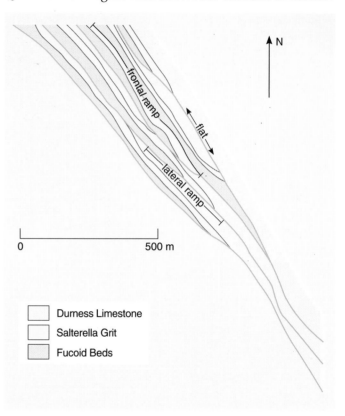

□ Durness Limestone
□ Salterella Grit
▨ Fucoid Beds

Figure A2.2 Answer to Question 2.4.

Figure A2.1 Answer to Question 2.3. The red hatched area shows a thrust-bounded block and the dashed red lines show an imbricate thrust.

Question 2.5 See Figure A2.3.

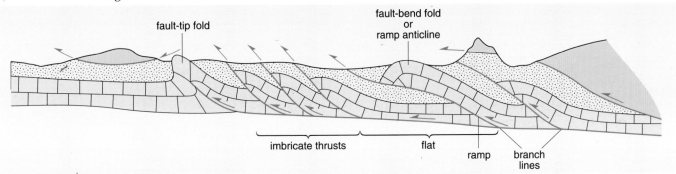

Figure A2.3 Answer to Question 2.5.

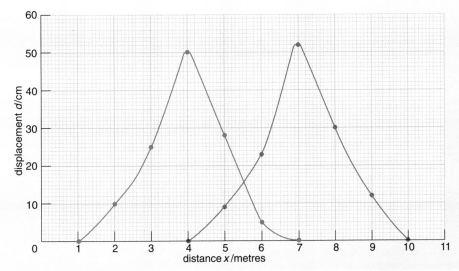

Figure A2.4 Answer to Question 2.6.

Question 2.6 Figure A2.4 is the completed graph and shows a typical overlap between displacements defining the transfer zone.

Question 2.7 The Cretaceous sequence is approximately 1.75 km thick and if that is repeated four times in the duplex, the limestone beneath it could be buried to 7 km depth. Given the quoted geotherm, this equates to a maximum temperature of 210 °C.

Question 2.8 The sedimentary thrust slices of the Sub-Alpine Chains are formed, in part, from sediments that originally constituted the cover to the External Crystalline Massifs.

Question 2.9 Fault-bend folds form in the hanging-wall of thrust above a ramp and its neighbouring flat. They are the deflections of the bedding that are necessary in order to keep the hanging-wall rocks in contact with the thrust plane during movement of the fault. A fault-tip fold forms ahead of a propagating thrust plane. It reflects the amount of ductile deformation that the rock can accommodate prior to fracturing.

Question 3.1 See Table A3.1.

Table A3.1 Answer to Question 3.1.

	folded layer profile shape	interlimb angle	axial plane fabric
Sub-Alpine Chains	parallel	open to close	no
Inner Zone thrust sheets	similar	close to tight	yes

Question 3.2 The Iltay Boundary Slide in the Ben Lui area shows a normal sense of displacement, because younger rocks are present in the hanging-wall, overlying older rocks in the footwall. The Ballachulish, Blair Atholl and Islay sub-Groups are missing, totalling 7.3 km of succession.

Question 3.3 It is likely that extensional structures in a collision zone either pre- or post-date the main shortening events. Those that are early in the sequence could be associated with the pattern of sedimentation that preceded the tectonics. Those that are later may relate to the instability of the thickened lithosphere that resulted from the shortening process.

Question 3.4 Horizon A: 10 m, 20 m, 30 m; horizon B: 10, 20, 30 m; horizon C: 0, 10, 20 m; horizon D: 0, 0, 10 m.

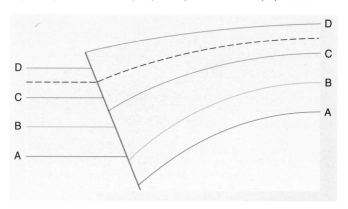

Figure A3.1 Answer to Question 3.4.

Question 3.5 The foliation planes are the most likely candidates, principally on the grounds that they are planar features that developed during the course of the shearing deformation.

Question 3.6 We need to assume that the foliation shown was produced by the shear zone deformation. The compass bearing of the foliation traces in the centre of the zone trends approximately 025° and this would correspond to the orientation of the zone itself. If there is no foliation present beyond that marked on the map, the width of the zone, measured at right-angles to the shear plane, is about 20 km. However, it appears that the intrusion of the Great Dyke, which occupies the eastern side of the map, truncated the shear zone and therefore the original width of the zone may have been greater.

Question 3.7 The fold can be described as a tight (an interlimb angle of less than 30°), asymmetric, antiform/synform pair. (i) The layers show significant thickening in the hinge area, the shape having even more hinge thickening than that associated with similar folds. (ii) The fold shape varies dramatically when traced from layer to layer with the amplitude varying from zero (i.e. unfolded layers) to a maximum and then back to zero again.

Question 3.8 Folds form at several places in the deforming cloth and they are of various sizes both in terms of amplitude and in lateral extent, and rarely extend all the way across the cloth. Their axes are approximately perpendicular to the direction of movement but, in detail, they curve around either side of this direction.

Question 3.9 The folds can be described as tight (an interlimb angle of between 0° and 30°), asymmetric, antiforms and synforms. The layers show some thickening in the hinge area, but not quite as much as that associated with similar folds. The fold shape is fairly constant from layer to layer.

Question 3.10

Outer Zone thrust sheet	Inner Zone fold nappe
Negligible metamorphism	At least greenschist facies metamorphism
Tectonic fabrics absent or poorly developed	Planar and linear fabrics well developed
Folding localized close to faults and related to fault propagation and movement	Folding developed at various scales throughout the nappe
Brittle deformation mechanisms predominate	Ductile deformation mechanisms predominate

Question 3.11 Deformation of grains by the crystal plastic processes that operate in mylonites causes an increase in the density of lattice dislocations. As the deformation proceeds, these dislocations become concentrated in specific parts of the grains, stacking up to produce sub-grain walls. These sub-grains eventually become sufficiently well established to behave as independent grains and consequently the grain size of the rock is reduced.

Question 3.12 If shear zones have a near-horizontal orientation, they act as ductile thrusts, allowing the crust to shorten by the stacking of nappes. If they are steeply dipping, they act as ductile strike–slip faults.

Question 4.1 These lines are slickensides. They are grooves that mark the direction of relative movement of the blocks on either side of the fault plane.

Question 4.2 The minor shear planes make an angle of around 40° to the fault zone walls and are thus R-shears. They have a consistently dextral shear sense and this must match that of the entire zone. Therefore, the fault is displacing the western block northwards with respect to the eastern one.

Question 4.3 We can look at both two- and three-dimensional features. In 2D, the direction in which a ramp cross-cuts the stratigraphy and the direction taken by branching thrusts are significant (Figure 2.9). In the third dimension, the identification of frontal and lateral ramps gives information on the sense of movement (Figure 2.13).

Question 4.4 The imbricate thrusts all ramp up from bottom right to top left. Therefore, the sense of movement is that the hanging-wall has moved to the left with respect to the footwall.

Question 4.5 The shear zone shows sinistral, top-to-the left sense of movement based on the curvature of the foliation trace.

Question 4.6 Figure A4.1 is an annotated sketch of the fold showing vergence direction. The vergence is towards the north-east.

Figure A4.1 Answer to Question 4.6.

Question 4.7 See Figure A4.2.

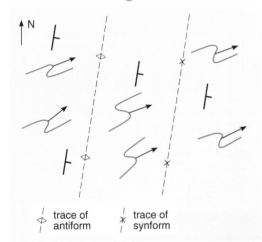

Figure A4.2 Answer to Question 4.7.

Question 4.8 The cleavage vergence direction is towards the east. Figure A4.3 shows the completed folds.

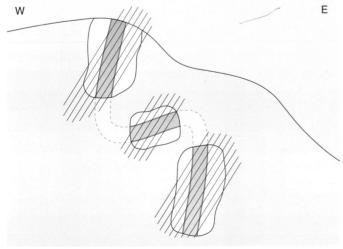

Figure A4.3 Answer to Question 4.8.

Question 4.9 (a) The kinematics of a brittle fault zone are determined from the orientation of the fault planes, the offset of marker horizons and the directions of slickensides present on the surface of the fault plane. The pattern of minor fractures (riedel shears) adds to this information. (b) The shear direction of a ductile shear zone is determined from the orientation of the planar and linear fabrics. Shear sense can be determined by using one or more of the following: fold asymmetry, asymmetric porphyroclasts, S-C fabrics.

Question 4.10 Fold vergence can be determined for any pair of asymmetric folds. By determining the sense of rotation needed to bring a long limb into the same orientation as a short limb, the compass direction pointed to by the upper arrow can be identified and this is the vergence direction of the folds.

Question 4.11 The method of establishing fold vergence assumes that it is the short limb of the fold pair that has rotated through the vertical and become inverted. However, when smaller fold pairs lie on the inverted limb of a larger fold, this assumption is invalid and the short limb is actually the right way up. In this case, cleavage vergence will give the opposite result to fold vergence.

Question 5.1 The terms antiform and synform refer to upward- and downward-closing folds respectively, whilst the use of the terms anticline and syncline requires that we can identify the relative ages of the folded units. An anticline must have the stratigraphically oldest units in the core of the fold whilst the youngest units must be in the core of a syncline.

Question 5.2 See Figure A5.1.

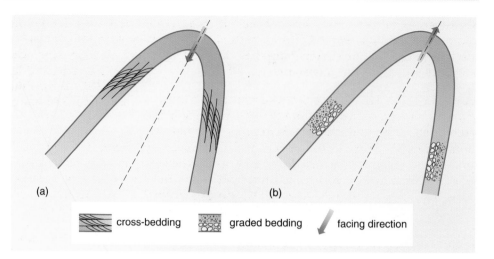

Figure A5.1 Answer to Question 5.2.

Question 5.3 See Figure A5.2.

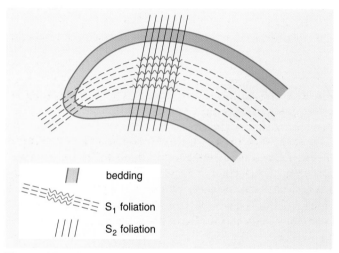

Figure A5.2 Answer to Question 5.3.

Question 5.4 The facing direction of a fold is the direction, traced along the axial plane, that will bring you into younger beds.

Question 5.5 Refer back to Figure 5.11.

Question 5.6 The critical evidence for two discrete deformation events would be examples of fabrics that show a consistent axial planar relationship with folds of one orientation, whilst themselves being folded by a differently oriented set. Shear zone folds, on the other hand, whilst commonly folding pre-existing fabrics, develop a variety of orientations during their formation and do not show a systematic relationship between fold orientation and the timing of fabric development.

Question 6.1 Geotherm (1) is a straight line and represents no crustal heat production and high mantle heat flow. Geotherm (2) is for heat production evenly distributed in the crust with no mantle heat flow (i.e. the geotherm is vertical below the Moho). Geotherm (3) is a mixture of both.

Question 6.2 From Figure 6.4, the rate of burial = 30/4 km per Ma = 7.5 km per Ma = 7.5 mm yr^{-1}.

Question 6.3 (a) Below the thrust, temperatures are low at high pressures. Above the thrust, we would have higher-temperature metamorphism. (b) The only way to preserve such a situation is through rapid exhumation soon after thrusting.

Question 6.4 Figure 6.14 shows a porphyroblast of garnet that clearly encloses rotated trails of inclusions. It is therefore syn-kinematic. Figure 6.15 contains a fractured porphyroblast of kyanite which is pre-kinematic.

Question 6.5 (a) At 600 °C the sillimanite field extends from about 230 to about 580 MPa. (b) Along A–B, the equilibrium is kyanite $\rightleftharpoons$ andalusite. (c) For C–D, the stable Al$_2$SiO$_5$ phase is andalusite; for D–E, it is sillimanite. (d) The area A–B–D–C defines the stability field of muscovite, quartz and andalusite, so the maximum possible pressure is about 370 MPa and the maximum temperature is about 615 °C.

Question 6.6 Kyanite, because it is stable at the highest pressures. The densities (in kg m^{-3}) are 3.55×10^3, 3.25×10^3, 3.15×10^3 for kyanite, sillimanite and andalusite respectively.

Question 6.7 From Figure 6.19, the assemblage cordierite, garnet, sillimanite and quartz could be stable at pressures from 300 MPa (in Fe-rich rocks) to 600 MPa (in Mg-rich rocks).

Question 6.8 (Fe/Mg) for garnet = 4, for biotite = 1 and for cordierite = 0.25. From Figure 6.20, the temperature for (Fe/Mg)$_{ga}$/(Fe/Mg)$_{biot}$ = 4 is about 700 °C. From Figure 6.19, the pressure for (Fe/Mg)$_{cord}$ = 0.25 at 700 °C is about 520 MPa, assuming a linear relationship between (Fe/Mg)$_{cord}$ and pressure.

Question 6.9 The geotherm passes through zeolite, prehnite–pumpellyite, greenschist, amphibolite and granulite facies successively with increasing depth.

Question 6.10 (a) The maximum pressure is reached 30 Ma earlier in the thrusting model. By the time the crust thickened homogeneously has reached its maximum thickness, the crust doubled by thrust tectonics is already being exhumed. (b) Peak temperatures are reached 37 Ma later in the homogeneous thickening model.

Question 6.11   (a) Heating can result from: (i) intrusion of magma by convection; (ii) fluid flow by convection; (iii) radioactive decay within thickened crust by conduction; (iv) thrusting (at the surfaces of footwall rocks) followed by conduction. Heating also results from crustal extension because thinning the crust brings mantle temperatures closer to the surface thus steepening the geothermal gradient. (b) Cooling can result from (i) uplift and erosion (exhumation) followed by conduction; and (ii) thrusting (at the base of nappes) followed by conduction.

Question 6.12   (a) The precise composition of each mineral would be needed together with a knowledge of experimental studies on the stability fields for which these minerals are stable. Strictly speaking, textural studies are needed to confirm that the minerals are in equilibrium (i.e. they all formed at the same time). (b) Textural studies are needed on a thin-section scale to determine the shapes of minerals and interpret their growth relative to local deformation. On outcrop scale, field observations are required to link the deformation fabric (cleavage, schistosity, etc.) to regional events.

Question 6.13   Mineral assemblages generally record the P–T field of their highest grade (maximum temperature). This will be reached, not on the steady-state geotherm before the crustal thickening event, but some time after thickening during exhumation, when heating due to crustal thickening is balanced by cooling as the surface is approached (see Figure 6.23). The resulting metamorphic geotherm connects a series of P–T fields formed at slightly different times. Consequently, it is neither a true transient geotherm nor a steady-state geotherm.

Question 7.1   On the Tibetan side, we should find evidence for an old active continental margin with extensive Andean-type magmatism. On the Indian side, within the Himalaya, there should be evidence for an old passive continental margin.

Question 7.2   Very well. Rifting of India from Gondwanaland occurred during the Cretaceous and India drifted north while Tethys was being subducted until collision 40–50 Ma ago. Magmatism therefore continued from the beginning of India's northward movement until about 10 Ma after collision.

Question 7.3   The TiO_2 vs. Zr plot indicates all the magmas are from a volcanic arc. The K_2O vs. SiO_2 plot suggests KV1 is a low-K basalt, typical of tholeiitic rocks. KV2 and KV3 are a basalt and andesite respectively, typical of the calc-alkaline trend. The FeO/MgO vs. SiO_2 plot confirms this trend. Taken together, the geochemical data suggest a maturing island arc.

Question 7.4   If there is no input from continental sediments, initial $^{87}Sr/^{86}Sr$ ratios should remain constant with time. However, an increasing role from subducted sediments should lead to a progressive increase in initial $^{87}Sr/^{86}Sr$. At the time of writing, there is no evidence for a sedimentary input into the Kohistan batholith.

Question 7.5   One granitic vein is highly folded and is cross-cut by an undeformed vein. So, the relative chronology is (i) intrusion of the early vein, (ii) deformation, (iii) intrusion of the second vein. As the deformation is bracketed by the intrusion events which are dated at 80–90 Ma, then the deformation is also in this age bracket.

Question 7.6   Major thrust and strike–slip sense earthquakes occur along the northern rim of the plateau in the Kunlun. In contrast, the plateau itself is characterized by normal and strike–slip fault-plane solutions. This fits the model well — with gravity spreading in the heart of the region and active compression on the flanks of the plateau.

Question 7.7   Pillow lavas form at, or slightly below, sea-level. So their present elevation of 4000 m requires an average surface uplift rate of 4000 m in 50 Ma. This is equal to 4×10^6 mm in 50×10^6 years or 0.08 mm yr^{-1}.

Question 7.8   From north to south the faults are the South Tibetan Detachment System (STDS) and the three thrust zones: the Main Central Thrust (MCT), the Main Boundary Thrust (MBT) and the Main Frontal Thrust (MFT). The MFT is the northern boundary of the foreland, the foothills thrust belt lies between the MBT and MFT. Between the MBT and the MCT are the Lesser Himalaya formations and between the MCT and the STDS are the High Himalaya formations (high-grade metamorphic rocks). North of the STDS lies the Tethyan sediments of the old Indian continental margin, which continue up to the suture.

Question 7.9   (a) The MCT is folded by the thrust sheet carried by the MBT, hence the MCT pre-dates the MBT. This suggests that thrusting migrated onto the foreland in a piggy-back sequence (Section 5.2). (b) The offset of each thrust is about 125 km giving a total shortening value of about 250 km.

Question 7.10   In the top slab or thrust sheet we would see a normal geotherm: increase of temperature with pressure. But as we approached the bottom slab or basement we would expect to see a decrease in temperature with depth (Figure 6.8). This is called an inverted metamorphic gradient.

Question 7.11   Uplift must have been very rapid to preserve the saw-tooth effects induced shortly after overthrusting, before the geotherm relaxed into a more conventional form (see Figure 6.8).

Question 7.12   The $[Fe/Mg]_{ga}/[Fe/Mg]_{bi}$ in the core is 7.0 and at the rim ~4.0. These ratios are equivalent to temperatures of ~550 °C and ~700 °C. The garnet then grew through an increase in temperature of 150 °C.

Question 7.13   From the equation for partial melting in Block 2:

$$C_l/C_0 = 1/(D + F (1-D))$$
$$370/150 = 1/(0.30 + F (1-0.30))$$
$$0.405 = 0.30 + F (1-0.30)$$
$$F = 0.105/0.70$$
$$= 0.15 \text{ (2 sig. figs)}$$

So, melting 15% of the schist would account for Rb enrichment in the granite melt.

Question 7.14   The sillimanite-grade data plots in a field of 400–700 MPa and 700–800 °C. This field lies up-temperature of both the wet and dry solidi on Figure 7.35 so granites could form either under hydrous conditions or by muscovite dehydration melting (Equation 7.1).

Question 7.15   At the time the melts formed (24–19 Ma), the source rocks were being rapidly exhumed along the STDS. Moreover, the decompression path of Figure 7.29 crosses the dehydration melt reaction for muscovite (Figure 7.35) suggesting that the drop in pressure triggered melting.

Question 7.16   The cooling rate along the east of the section was 200 °C in 24 Ma determined from the zircon data (8.3 °C Ma^{-1}) or 125 °C in 11 Ma (11.4 °C Ma^{-1}) determined from apatite data. The maximum cooling rate occurs on the western edge of the syntaxis because the ages when closure was reached are younger than in the east. This, together with the asymmetric form of the fission track profiles, suggests that uplift is occurring much faster on the western flank of the syntaxis.

Question 7.17   They are antiforms — folding up the higher thrust sheets and exposing structurally lower rocks in their cores.

Acknowledgements

Every effort has been made to trace all copyright owners, but if any has been inadvertently overlooked, we will be pleased to make the necessary arrangements at the first opportunity. Grateful acknowledgement is made to the following sources for permission to reproduce material in this Block:

Figure 1.2 Hoffman, P. F. (1999) *Journal of African Earth Science*, **28**(1), p.19 Elsevier Science; *Figure 1.5* illustration by Tom Prentiss from 'The break-up of Pangaea', *Continents Adrift (Readings from Scientific American)*, Scientific American © 1970 N. H. Prentiss; *Figure 1.6* P. Patrait and J. Achache (1984) 'India–Eurasia collision chronology', *Nature*, **311**, 18 Oct., Macmillan; *Figures 2.5, 2.10, 3.5, 3.18, 4.4, 4.6, 4.9, 4.12a, 7.11* kindly provided by Rob Butler, University of Leeds; *Figures 2.14, 2.27, 3.1, 3.2, 3.6, 3.19d, 3.22, 3.26, 3.30–3.32, 4.14, 5.7, 5.9* kindly provided by John Whalley, University of Portsmouth; *Figure 2.17d* NASA; *Figures 2.20, 2.22, 5.12* R. D. Hatcher (1990) *Geology: Principles, Concepts and Problems*, Columbus Merrill Publishing Co., Pearson Education; *Figure 2.21* 'Surge zones in the Moine thrust zone, Scotland', *Journal of Structural Geology*, **4**(3), p.251 © 1982 Elsevier Science; *Figure 2.23* R. Gillcrist, M. Coward and J. Mugnier (1987) *Geodinamica Acta*, **1**(1), Editions Elsevier, France; *Figure 2.25* 'Displacement geometry in the volume containing a small fault', *AAPG Bulletin*, **71**(1), Aug. 1987, AAPG; *Figure 3.3* kindly provided by Chris Hawkesworth, University of Bristol; *Figure 3.6* Aerographica/Patricia & Angus Macdonald; *Figures 3.7, 3.8* J. L. Roberts and J. E. Treagus, 'Stratigraphical and structural correlation between the Dalradian rocks of the South-West and Central Highland of Scotland', in A. L. Harris, C. H. Holland and B. E. Leake (1979) *The Caledonides of the British Isles – Reviewed*, Scottish Academic Press; *Figure 3.11* S. M. Reddy, J. Wheeler and R. A. Cliff (1999) 'The geometry and timing of orogenic extension', *Journal of Metamorphic Geology*, **17**(5), Blackwell Science Inc.; *Figure 3.12* J. Epard and A. Escher (1996) 'Transition basement to cover: a geometric model', *Journal of Structural Geology*, **18**(5), p.543, Elsevier Science; *Figure 3.15* J. G. Ramsay and M. I. Huber (1983) 'Session 1, Displacement', *The Techniques of Modern Structural Geology*, Vol. 1, *Strain Analysis*, p.2 © 1983 Academic Press;

Figure 3.17 adapted from Fig. 12, p. 328, Coward, M. P. (1976) 'Archaean deformation patterns in southern Africa', *Philosophical Transactions of the Royal Society of London, A*, Vol. 283, The Royal Society; *Figure 3.20* kindly supplied by Tom Argles; *Figure 3.21* Hobbs, B. E., Means, W. D. and Williams, P. F. (1976) *An Outline of Structural Geology*, John Wiley & Sons Inc. © 1976 the authors; *Figure 3.29* G. I. Alsop and R. E. Holdsworth (1999) 'Vergence and facing patterns in large scale sheath folds', *Journal of Structural Geology*, **21**, p.1345 © 1999 Elsevier Science; *Figure 4.6* R. W. H. Butler (1982) 'The terminology of structures in thrust belts', *Journal of Structural Geology*, **4**(3), p. 244 © 1982 Elsevier Science (review article originally presented in poster form at Annual Meeting of Tectonic Studies Group (Geological Society, London) at Oxford University, Dec. 1981); *Figure 4.8* D. Elliot (1976) 'The energy balance and deformation mechanics of thrust sheets', *Philosophical Transactions of the Royal Society of London, A*, **283**, The Royal Society; *Figure 4.11* C. Simpson and S. M. Schmid (1983) 'An evaluation of criteria to deduce the sense of movement in sheared rocks', *Geological Society of America Bulletin*, **94**, Nov., The Geological Society of America; *Figure 4.12b* G. S. Lister (1984) 'S-C mylonites', *Journal of Structural Geology*, **6**(6), p.619 © 1984 Elsevier Science; *Figure 5.11* C. D. A. Dahlstrom (1970) 'Structural geology in the eastern margin of the Canadian Rocky Mountains', *Bulletin of Canadian Petroleum Geology*, **18**, Canadian Society of Petroleum Geologists; *Figure 5.13* J. G. Ramsay and M. I. Huber (1987) *The Techniques of Modern Structural Geology*, Vol. 2, *Folds and Fractures*, 'Session 24', p. 556, © 1987 Academic Press London; *Figures 6.9 and 6.11* © Kevin Jones; *Figures 6.10, 6.12, 6.13* Spry, A. (1979) *Metamorphic Textures*, Pergamon Press Ltd, © 1979 A. Spry; *Figure 7.1* US National Intelligence Mapping Agency, GTOPO30 digital elevation data, map designed by Steve Drury; *Figure 7.13a* NASA; *Figure 7.17* © Nick Arnaud; *Figure 7.21* Zhao *et al.* (1993) 'Deep seismic reflection evidence for continental underthrusting beneath southern Tibet', *Nature*, **366**(9) Dec. © 1993 Macmillan; *Figure 7.36* N. Harris and J. Massey (1994) *Tectonics*, **13**(6), p. 1539, © 1994 American Geophysical Union; *Figure 7.43* R. W. H. Butler (1988) 'Flashfloods, earthquakes and uplift in the Pakistan Himalaya', *Geology Today*, **4**(6), Blackwell Science Ltd.

Index

Note: bold page numbers denote where Glossary terms are introduced/defined